YORK NOTE

General Editors: Professor A.N. Jenares (*University of Stirling*) & Professor Suheil Bushrui (*American University of Beirut*)

Aldous Huxley

BRAVE NEW WORLD

Notes by Michael Routh

MA (CALIFORNIA STATE UNIVERSITY, LONG BEACH)
PH D (WISCONSIN)
Lecturer in English, University of Utrecht

LONGMAN
YORK PRESS

YORK PRESS
Immeuble Esseily, Place Riad Solh, Beirut.

LONGMAN GROUP UK LIMITED
Longman House, Burnt Mill, Harlow,
Essex CM20 2JE, England
Associated companies, branches and representatives
throughout the world

First published 1982
Eleventh impression 1993

ISBN 0-582-03355-1

Produced by Longman Singapore Publishers Pte Ltd
Printed in Singapore

Contents

Part 1

Introduction

The life of Aldous Huxley

Aldous (Leonard) Huxley was born into an upper-middle-class English family in Surrey in 1894. After an apparently happy childhood, he was sent to Eton College in 1908, where he studied biology with the intention of becoming a medical doctor. There, one month after his arrival, he was to suffer the first great shock of his early life—the death from cancer of his mother, to whom young Aldous had been particularly close. Barely two months later, Huxley was jolted once again when an eye disease left him virtually blind. However, following surgery and mastery of Braille (the touch-alphabet used by the blind) Huxley entered Balliol College, Oxford, in 1913, to read literature. In 1916 he graduated with a first in English literature, an amazing achievement considering his handicap. Meanwhile, in 1914, Huxley suffered the third great shock of his youth when his brother Trevenen, who had helped Aldous during his blindness, committed suicide in a fit of depression.

Huxley's first book, a collection of poems entitled *The Burning Wheel*, was published in 1916. Three more volumes of verse and a collection of stories followed rapidly, but it was not until the publication in 1921 of his first novel, the satirical *Crome Yellow*, that Huxley won significant critical attention. Several more satires followed in the 1920s, during which time Huxley also wrote a considerable amount of journalism (essays, reviews, and articles for popular magazines) as well as book-length non-fiction (essays and travel books). For most of the decade Huxley lived in Italy; but by the early 1930s, when he had written *Brave New World* (published 1932), he was living in the south of France and continuing to produce fiction and essays. In 1937 Huxley moved to Los Angeles, hoping that the climate would improve his eyesight. His writing betrayed his interest in Eastern mysticism and his attempts to reconcile Eastern thought with Western science, until he died of cancer in 1963.

Huxley's ancestry

Few writers have come to their profession with as impressive an ancestry as Aldous Huxley. Dr Leonard Huxley, his father, was an educator, a biographer of famous scientists, and the editor of the *Cornhill Magazine*—previous editors included the novelist William Makepeace

Thackeray (1811–63) and the critic Sir Leslie Stephen (1832–1904)—which published the work of such leading Victorian writers as Matthew Arnold, John Ruskin, and Anthony Trollope. Aldous Huxley's mother, Julia, one of the first women to graduate from the University of Oxford, was an excellent and innovative teacher and the founder of a successful girls' school. On his mother's side Huxley's great-grandfather was Dr Thomas Arnold, the most famous educator of Victorian England (he had reformed the public school system in the first part of the nineteenth century) and a clergyman who believed in infusing morality into a liberal education. Dr Arnold's son, and a grandfather of Aldous Huxley, also named Thomas, taught at a Catholic university with the poet Gerard Manley Hopkins. One of Huxley's aunts of whom Aldous was especially fond was Mrs Humphry Ward, a moralistic novelist and a social reformer. But certainly the two most significant of Aldous Huxley's ancestors were his grandfather on his father's side—the scientist T. H. Huxley (1825–95)—and his great-uncle on his mother's side, the poet Matthew Arnold (1822–66). Their influence helped to shape the direction of Huxley's work. Their careers exhibited the dominant conflict Aldous Huxley would incorporate into much of his own writing, including *Brave New World*: the tension between science and art.

T. H. Huxley, Aldous's paternal grandfather, began his career as a medical doctor and widely-acclaimed biologist. After achieving fame in the middle of the nineteenth century as 'Darwin's Bulldog' for defending the theory of evolution published in *The Origin of Species* (1859) against the clergy's biblically-based views, Huxley began to focus more and more on popularising science with the masses, and, as a corollary, with the direction modern education ought to take. While not denying a need for the humanities (he learned French, German, Italian, and Greek on his own, and believed that the ability to write well was indispensable for the scientist), Huxley argued that science should be given prominence in education: he wanted, he said, a 'scientific education'.

Huxley debated this position publicly with Matthew Arnold, his great-uncle. Arnold, who had largely stopped writing poetry by the mid-1850s to concentrate on literary criticism and the study of society, asserted that each culture is ultimately evaluated chiefly on its position in the humanities, its contribution to 'the best that is known and thought in the world'. Consequently, he held that the humanities should be given primacy over the sciences in a wise educational system.

Although *Brave New World* was written half a century after the Huxley-Arnold debate, this clash of ideas is significant to Aldous Huxley's novel (and, indeed, to Huxley's work in general) in several respects. Firstly, the collision between art and science, which can be extended to include a collision between reason and imagination and between matter and spirit, generates the central tension that Bernard

Marx, Helmholtz Watson, and John Savage experience in *Brave New World* between over-regulation of the individual and the need for spiritual fulfilment. As Mustapha Mond, one of the World State's ten controllers, realises, science and art can both be liberating forces if allowed free play—but they can also be forces of control: science by determining the genetic constitution of humanity, and art by formulating socially-desirable rules into memorable aphorisms that people take to be truths and then act upon. Secondly, the intense belief in the value of education shared by T. H. Huxley and Matthew Arnold is shown also by Aldous Huxley in *Brave New World*. Used wrongly, as it is in sleep-teaching, education warps individuals into thoughtless tools of the social body; used properly, it can lead to the spiritual illuminations the Savage is blessed with through his reading of Shakespeare. Thirdly, the debate format, carried out by means of public lectures—in which, for example, Arnold's 'Literature and Science' (1883) answered T. H. Huxley's 'Science and Culture' (1880)—provides Aldous Huxley with a literary vehicle to which he returns again and again. In *Brave New World*, the debate-lecture technique is most prominent in the confrontation between Mond and the Savage toward the end of the novel. Moreover, this device leads to consideration of *Brave New World* as a 'novel of ideas' (discussed in Part 3).

The cultural milieu

Although *Brave New World* is set six hundred years after its date of publication, Huxley, like most writers of utopias (see Part 3), is actually commenting on contemporary social conditions and behaviour. Hence some understanding of the 1920s, the decade that Huxley is to a large extent criticising in *Brave New World*, should help to illuminate Huxley's social satire.

Writing in London in 1920, Ezra Pound summed up the intellectual despair and disillusionment that would become a major force of the decade that has come to be known as the 'Roaring Twenties': Western culture is an 'old bitch gone in the teeth', a 'blotched civilisation'. At the foundation of this pessimism lay the shadow of the First World War (1914–18)—a futile, savage, senseless war fought, essentially, for the grossest of possible motives, money. This war shattered the long-established social structure of Europe; brought to an abrupt halt a century of relative peace, since no major wars had been fought since the Napoleonic Wars ended in 1815; was the first 'modern' war in that it was the first to employ awesome mechanical weapons, such as tanks and aeroplanes; destroyed the later-Victorian faith that science—which developed the terrible weapons of the First World War—could usher in an age of ever-progressive human improvement. Thus, by the 1920s, the

'Jazz Age', the 'Big Party', many people were left with a sense that they were living in a moral vacuum, that old values and beliefs had been rendered impotent without being replaced by new, vital ones. In *Crome Yellow*, published three years after the First World War was concluded, one character comments on the 'horrors' that 'are taking place in every corner of the world. People are being crushed, slashed, disembowelled, mangled; their dead bodies rot and their eyes decay with the rest. Screams of pain and fear go pulsing through . . .' Yet even such horrors as these are taken 'all for granted. Since the war we wonder at nothing.'

Many people, therefore, felt that under such distressing circumstances, the only reasonable course of action was to try to see and do as much as possible before the fabric of society gave way entirely. Such a mode of life, understandably, yielded hedonism and cynicism. 'Conspicuous consumption'—the public display of unnecessary and excessive but trivial spending—was one hedonistic way that those who could afford it might relieve spiritual emptiness. So was sexual promiscuity. Another method for confronting the unsettling times was to assume a mocking, cynical tone. If nothing is worthwhile or sacred after all, then no significant action can be taken, and thinking about how bad things are is by definition an exercise in futility – better to enjoy ourselves while we can; such was the outlook of many of the young.

The hedonistic and cynical elements of futuristic London in *Brave New World*, then, can be seen as commentaries on the decade that Huxley had just lived through (and which, indeed, he satirised in several novels written during these ten years). Therefore, when we are informed early in *Brave New World* that an appreciation of nature is socially undesirable because it does nothing to keep the financial cogs of industry spinning, and that games requiring expensive equipment that is to be thrown away when damaged rather than to be repaired ('Ending is better than mending') are therefore preferable, we are meant to apply the implied cultural criticism to Huxley's own society. The same is true of the novel's sexual theme: the implied criticism of the socially-sanctioned promiscuity of AF 632 London is meant to be applied to contemporary Britain. The cynicism displayed by Mond, who contends that 'civilisation has absolutely no need of nobility or heroism', is likewise intended to reflect the empty values of Huxley's own day.

A note on the text

Brave New World was first published by Chatto & Windus, London, 1932. The standard edition is that published by Chatto & Windus in 1970 as part of the Collected Edition of Huxley's work. Page references in these Notes are to the inexpensive, readily-available Panther paperback edition: *Brave New World*, Granada, London, 1977.

Part 2

Summaries
of BRAVE NEW WORLD

A general summary

After the fantastical futuristic setting of the novel is presented in the first several chapters, the action begins as Bernard Marx, a highly intelligent but awkward and eccentric man who is dissatisfied with life, takes Lenina Crowne for a holiday to the Savage Reservation in New Mexico. They bring back to London with them John Savage, who was born at the Reservation, and his mother, Linda, a former worker in the Brave New World who by mischance has had to spend the past several years at the Reservation. Bernard proudly parades the primitive Savage before the curious eyes of the overly-civilised Londoners until the Savage protests. Meanwhile, Linda has been put in hospital and is dying. The Savage rushes to her side, feeling guilty for having abandoned her. Linda dies; on his way out of the hospital the Savage incites a riot and is arrested, along with Bernard and Helmholtz Watson, a mutual friend and, like Bernard, an eccentric. Mustapha Mond, the controller in charge of London, lectures the three men on the need for individual conformity and social stability, then exiles Bernard and Helmholtz. The Savage, however, escapes. For a brief time he is happy living alone in the English countryside. But curiosity-seekers eventually find him, ruin his peace, and tempt him into participation in a furious orgy. Ashamed, the Savage hangs himself.

Detailed summaries

Foreword

Written fifteen years after *Brave New World*, the Foreword offers the following insights in retrospect:

(1) Between the extremes of the technologically-dominated London of AF632 and the primitivism of the Savage Reservation lay the possibility of using science in the context of a spiritually-centred community (a possibility Huxley would explore later, in his last novel, *Island* (1967)) (pp.7–8).

(2) The novel should not have neglected to incorporate nuclear energy into the Brave New World; but this oversight does not effect the main drive or meaning of the story (pp.9–10).

(3) Man must look within (to the human spirit) rather than without (to technology) to improve the world (p.10).
(4) He must decentralise political power before statism overwhelms the individual (pp.11–12).
(5) Should a new totalitarian state emerge, it will probably resemble the Brave New World in that it will govern not by force, but – through skilful use of propaganda – by convincing its population to love its own servitude (pp.12–14).
(6) 'All things considered, it looks as though Utopia were far closer to us than anyone, only fifteen years ago, could have imagined' (p.14).

NOTES AND GLOSSARY:

epigraph: 'Utopias appear to be a good deal more realisable than was previously thought. And we are today faced with an alarming question of a different nature: How to avoid their complete realisation? Utopias are realisable. Life moves towards utopias. And perhaps a new century is beginning, a century when intellectuals and the cultured class will dream of ways of avoiding utopias and of returning to a non-utopic society, less "perfect" and more free.' (Translated from the French by Keith Busby.) A Russian religious philosopher, Berdiaeff (1874–1948) believed in combining a transcendent mystical vision with social improvement, a combination that increasingly appealed to Huxley and that he made central to his last novel, *Island* (1962). Having been exiled from Russia in 1927, Berdiaeff was living in Paris when he wrote *Freedom and the Spirit* (1927), from which the above quotation is taken

Foreword: written in 1946 for the Collected Edition volume of *Brave New World*, which was published in 1950

Penitente: *(Latin)* repentant

Pyrrhonic: a follower of the thought of Pyrrhon (or Pyrrho) (*c*.360–*c*.272 BC), a Greek philosopher who held that, because man can know nothing with absolute certainty, it is wisest to suspend judgement and be indifferent to circumstances

aesthete: a lover of beauty for its own sake

fable a narrative, usually brief, with a clear moral that is usually stated at the end

Pantheon: a temple to the gods built in Rome in AD 2

ossuary: a vault containing bones of the dead

'*Si monumentum requiris circumspice*': *(Latin)* 'if you would seek his monument, look around you'; written by the son of the architect Christopher Wren (1632–1723) and inscribed above the interior of the North Door of St Paul's Cathedral, London, which Wren built. Huxley's satiric point here is that a mindless use of higher education has produced military weapons of great destructive power

Reservation: the Savage Reservation in *Brave New World*. Such a reservation is a tract of land set aside—'reserved'— by the United States government for use by the Indians, whose own land the government periodically confiscated during the nineteenth century as the country expanded westward; Huxley comments satirically on this practice in the novel

Henry-Georgian: a reference to Henry George (1839–97), an idealistic social reformer whose *Progress and Poverty* (1879) greatly influenced later nineteenth-century radical thought

Kroptkinesque: referring to the Russian Peter Kroptkin (1842–1921), an idealistic revolutionist

Sabbath: the seventh and last day of the week, used here in the secular sense to refer to a period of rest from the labour of the preceding six days

Tao: the 'road', or 'way', to truth in Chinese philosophy

Logos: the word incarnate in Jesus Christ

Brahmin: a member of the highest Hindu caste, the priestly caste

High Utilitarianism: utilitarianism, an essentially nineteenth-century social programme defining goodness as that which brings the greatest amount of happiness to the greatest number of people; Huxley's addition of the adjective 'High' suggests a spiritual application of this philosophy

nuclear fission: the splitting of atoms to release a tremendous amount of energy that can be used peaceably, to generate electricity, but also destructively, to produce atomic bombs

Robert Nichols: British poet and playwright (1893–1944)

Marquis de Sade: Count Donatien Alphonse François de Sade (1740–1814), a French novelist whose works described 'sadism'—a term, named after de Sade, for the experience of sexual pleasure by the infliction of pain or stress on another creature

Robespierre: Maximilien de Robespierre (1758–94), an extremist leader of the Jacobin Club, which vowed to carry out the goals of the French Revolution at all costs, regardless of consequences and without compromises

Babeuf: François Babeuf (1760–97), French revolutionary and journalist, whose *Conspiracy of Equals* (1796) called for universal equality of income

Thirty Years' War: a religious conflict (1618–48) begun between Catholics and Protestants, that expanded to include most of Europe in a political power struggle—at great cost to civilians, who were often mercilessly pillaged by soldiers

the fifth Marquess of Lansdowne: Henry Petty-Fitzmaurice (1845–1927), who expressed the idea of ending the First World War through negotiation with Germany (as opposed to through armed conflict) in a letter dated 29 November 1917, eventually printed in the *Daily Telegraph*

Bolshevism: the programme of the radical element of the 'Bolsheviks'—the Russian Social Democratic Party, led by Lenin (1870–1924), which controlled the government following the Russian Revolution (1917)

Fascism: an extremely authoritarian, anti-socialistic form of government, developed in Italy in the 1920s, that spread elsewhere in Europe, most notably to Spain and Germany

Hitler: Adolf Hitler (1889–1945), the German dictator whose Nazi Party murdered millions of Jews in the late 1930s and during the Second World War (1939–45)

Hiroshima: the Japanese city on which the first atomic bomb was dropped, on 6 August 1945

Magdeburg: a city in eastern Germany destroyed and pillaged in 1631, during the Thirty Years War (see above)

Procrustes: in Greek mythology, a character who forced guests to fit the bed he provided for them by stretching or cutting off the guests' legs

totalitarian: a dictatorial form of government in which all opposition is outlawed and the state has complete control over all facets of human life

statism: a political system characterised by a strong central government

the Holy Ghost: the spirit of God, the third element of the Christian Trinity (Father, Son, Holy Ghost); here used ironically

the Jesuits: followers of the Society of Jesus, a religious movement formed in Paris in 1534; their system of religious education is extremely demanding and rigorous

Voltaire: François Marie Arouet (1694–1778), a witty anti-clerical sceptic who greatly influenced the leaders of the French Revolution; Huxley's point here is that Voltaire's teachers failed miserably in their efforts to pass on to Voltaire their own traditional values

What Mr Churchill calls an 'iron curtain': Sir Winston Churchill (1874–1965), famous British Conservative states- man, first used the metaphor 'iron curtain' in a speech on 16 August 1945, to describe the forced isolation of the Soviet-bloc countries

Manhattan Projects: 'Manhattan Project' was the code name for the programme that developed the atomic bomb

scopolamine: a sedative (hyoscine)

eugenics: the systematic attempt to produce certain types of human beings

soma: a hypothetical drug, both sedative and euphoric, used to control the masses in *Brave New World*; the word was first used by August Weismann (1834–1914) as a label for those body cells not reproductive in nature; Chapter 8 of *Brave New World Revisited* relates soma to today's methods of 'chemical persuasion'

scientific caste system: a reference to the rigidly separated, inflexible social-class groupings in *Brave New World*, created by science

Chapter 1

Six hundred years into the future, a group of students is conducted on a tour of the Central London Hatchery and Conditioning Centre. As the obedient students move through the Fertilising, Bottling, and Social Predestination Rooms, the Director of Hatcheries and Conditioning and one of the scientists, Henry Foster, explain in detail the technological wonders of the Brave New World. Along the way, Henry makes a date with a pretty co-worker, Lenina Crowne. As the chapter ends, the students are heading toward the Decanting Room.

NOTES AND GLOSSARY:

fret-sawyers: a fret is an ornamental pattern cut from wood with a fret-saw, a thin-bladed, fine-toothed saw; here Huxley is being ironic, as he frequently is in the novel

A.F. 632: 632 years After Ford; that is, 600 years in the future (*Brave New World* was published in 1932). The industrialist Henry Ford (see below) gave his name to the new era, whereas Christ had been used to delineate the preceding era (AD: *Anno Domini (Latin)*, 'in the year of our Lord'). This is the first of numerous satires on the secularisation of the Brave New World

ova: egg-cells, here of the human female, which develop into embryos and are subsequently born as babies when fertilised by sperm from the male

gamete: mature sex cell

thermogene: heat produced by the human body

excised ovary: a reproductive organ that has been cut away from the female

salinity: salt content

viscosity: the density of a fluid, which defines its capacity to flow

spermatozoa: male sex cells

Alphas ... Epsilons: the five social and intellectual castes of the Brave New World, labelled by the names of the first five letters of the Greek alphabet

embryo: the state of pre-birth development, here of a human being

the old viviparous days: the time when babies were born directly from the wombs of their mothers, rather than being 'decanted' (see below), as they are in the Brave New World

largesse: money or gifts given to the masses by the rich

Singapore: a former British colony at the extreme south of the Malay Peninsula

Mombasa: the chief seaport of Kenya, in east Africa; this reference, along with those to Singapore (above) and other distant places throughout the novel, is meant to provide a sense of scope to the World State, whose political structure and workings are discussed only vaguely

pituitary: gland that secretes hormones (chemicals) affecting the growth of human beings

decanted: literally, the transfer of wine from its bottle to a jar or jug before being served; here, an ironic term suggesting that the new-born babies are poured out of the bottles in which they have spent their first nine months of life. Babies in the Brave New World are developed in the manner of a consumer product

sow's peritoneum: membrane lining the abdomen of a female pig; such a membrane is used in the Brave New World as a replacement for a natural mother's womb

morula: the mass of cells into which a fertilised egg divides

saline solution: salt solution

lupus: an ulcerous disease of the facial skin

like chickens ... eyes: lacking the muscles that automatically force liquid down the throats of humans, birds must lift their heads to swallow; Huxley's irony is obvious here

demijohns: large bottles with narrow necks and wide bodies, used for chemical processes such as fermentation

Two hundred and fifty-seven days: in other words, the nine-month gestation period preceding human birth

blood-surrogates: artificial blood on which the bottled embryos feed; the first of several such 'surrogates' in the novel that have replaced the natural with the man-made in the Brave New World

placentin: presumably, nutritive material supplied to the embryo which in natural circumstances would be done by the placenta

thyroxin: the hormone produced by the thyroid gland that influences growth and metabolism

corpus luteum: *(Latin)* 'deep, yellow-orange body'; a yellow gland formed in the ovary, which secretes a hormone vital to reproduction

centrifugal: a force spinning away from a central point

placenta: the tissue in a mother's womb through which the foetus (developing child) is nourished, and into which it discharges its waste products

anaemia: an inadequate number of red corpuscles in the blood, resulting in an insufficient supply of oxygen to the body

foetal foal's liver: liver (which produces red corpuscles) of the foetus of an ass or a horse. The dependence in the Brave New World on animal parts—here, in the reference to 'hog's stomach extract' immediately preceding, and elsewhere—is grimly satiric of the non-human method of reproduction of the Brave New World

gravity: seriousness

'trauma of decanting': a parody of the 'birth trauma' postulated by the Austrian psychoanalyst Otto Rank (1884–1939), according to which human birth is held to be a devastating experience after the comfortable security of the mother's womb

freemartins: more satire: a freemartin is a sterile cow or ox; Henry Foster will shortly speak with ironic pride of speeding up the physical development of human beings 'till it was as quick, say, as a cow's...!' (pp.23–4)

endocrine: a ductless hormone-producing gland; several endocrine glands, such as the thyroid and the pituitary, secrete hormones essential to bodily growth

germinal mutation: the genetic process whereby a new form, differing from its parents, is produced

acetate: a type of synthetic fabric; another indication of the artificiality of Brave New World existence

a row of coral teeth: perhaps a parody of the conventional poetic reference to 'pearly' teeth as a sign of beauty; indeed the description here of Lenina—with her appearance of a lupus skin condition and 'purple eyes' due to lighting—might parody the English poet Robert Browning (1812–92), whom Huxley considered overly optimistic: *The Pied Piper of Hamelin* mentions: 'little boys and girls,/ With rosy cheeks and flaxen curls,/ And sparkling eyes, and teeth like pearls'

caustic: corrosive; destructive of skin tissues

Chapter 2

In the Infant Nurseries, the students witness the conditioning of babies to fear and dislike nature and books. They also learn about sleep-teaching, by means of which Brave New World children have the World State's propagandistic slogans drummed into their unconscious, sleeping minds.

NOTES AND GLOSSARY:

Neo-Pavlovian conditioning: referring to the theory of 'classical conditioning' of the Russian physiologist Ivan Petrovich Pavlov (1849–1936), who found that dogs could be trained to respond to a stimulus organically unrelated to the response elicited; in the most famous of such experiments, by ringing a bell when he fed dogs, he eventually 'trained' the dogs to salivate at the sound of a bell alone; 'neo' ('new') because Pavlov's work took place over six centuries before the story. (See Chapter 7, 'Brainwashing', of *Brave New World Revisited* for a discussion of Pavlovian technique in our time)

apoplectic: suffering apoplexy, or stroke, which damages sense and motion

What man ... asunder: a parody of the Bible, Mark 10:9: 'What therefore God hath joined together, let no man put asunder'; in the Brave New World, man, misusing the powers of science, has become his own god

Our Ford: referring to the American Henry Ford (1863–1947), whose autobiography *My Life and Work* (1922) Huxley read in the mid-1920s and incorporates into the novel as the bible of the Brave New World (p.175). Ford was probably the most influential industrialist of the first half of the twentieth century, largely through his invention of moving assembly-line mass-production to build the Model T automobile (see below) in 1909—the main features of which are the use of standardised parts and the specialisation of the functions of workers. Thus Ford is the 'god' of the overly-standardised, overly-specialised world of mass-production that Huxley is attacking (see p.18). Conveniently for Huxley, Ford's name rhymes with 'lord' and throughout *Brave New World* is used in place of 'lord' and also of 'God', as in 'Our Ford', 'his fordship', and so on. A character in Huxley's *Point Counter Point* (1928) claims that, along with orthodox Christianity and mechanical science, 'Henry Ford's disease' (standardised mass-production) is 'killing' modern man

'a dead language': the one-state world has done away with all languages except English, revealing the monolithic nature of the Brave New World

smut: small piece of dirt; here, obscene publications

George Bernard Shaw: Shaw (1856–1950) is generally regarded as the greatest twentieth-century dramatist; his works have *not* been banned from the Brave New World, probably because of their iconoclastic attitude toward traditional values and because Shaw felt emotions to be a hindrance in economic matters

T-Model: the sturdy but simple Model T, Ford's most popular car; between its introduction in 1908, and 1927 when the last one was built, over 15,000,000 Model T's were sold, the last of them selling for less than half the price of the first ones, because of the increasing efficiency of mass-production

Here the Director ... stomach: in the Brave New World, the symbol of industrial progress, the 'T' (taken, of course, from the name of Ford's most popular car), has replaced the Christian cross; significantly, the Director makes the sign of the 'T' on his stomach, an organ of consumption, rather than on his heart, as Christians do. A similar replacement of the conventional Christian cross occurs in *Ape and Essence* (1948), a novel about a future much different from the overly-progressive Brave New World, in which nuclear destruction has reduced Los Angeles to a community of devil-worshippers who make the 'sign of the horns' on their brows

sibilant: a hissing sound

categorial imperative: an absolute moral decree; the term, from the philosophy of the German transcendentalist Immanuel Kant (1726–1804), is used ironically here

asafoetida: a strong, garlic-smelling plant secretion used medicinally

Chapter 3

This chapter, stylistically the most experimental of the novel, alternates between scenes taking place outdoors and scenes taking place indoors. In the outdoor scenes, the students continue their guided tour by watching children being sexually conditioned to accept and participate in erotic games as a matter of course, without concerning themselves with moral questions or emotional attachments to sexual partners. Mustapha Mond, one of the ten controllers of the World State, suddenly appears. He lectures the students on the evils of family life and the benefits of social security. He also provides a brief 'history' of the Brave New World from the twentieth century to AF632 (even though Mond earlier has quoted Henry Ford that 'history is bunk'). Simultaneously, indoors in the Men's Dressing Room, the eccentric Bernard Marx is nauseated by Henry Foster's casual attitude toward his (Foster's) sexual relationship with Lenina Crowne; while in the Women's Dressing Room, Lenina is revealing to her friend Fanny an unconventionally monogamous sexual loyalty to one man, Henry Foster, but also admitting her attraction toward Bernard. In the Infant Nurseries, children are being sleep-taught Brave New World propaganda.

NOTES AND GLOSSARY:

boskage: a wooded area

most games ... netting: referring to cricket, football, hockey, etc.

surreptitious auto-erotism: secret, self-induced sexual activity; in other words, masturbation in private

discarnate: disembodied; official communication in the Brave New World is often made through similarly non-human means, especially through the use of synthetic voices (see Part 3)

'History is Bunk': 'bunk' is slang for nonsense; these words were spoken by Henry Ford in 1919, and 613 years later they well describe the live-for-the-present philosophy of the Brave New World. The catalogue that follows this quotation consists of culturally-significant civilisations, people, gods, and creations from the historical and mythological past that (like all things historical) have been dismissed from the Brave New World as being irrelevant to the present, and also dangerous because of the power for change they represent

Harappa: a city of the ancient Indus Valley civilisation

Ur of the Chaldees: see the Old Testament (Genesis 11:28,31) for Ur, an ancient Mesopotamian city of the Chaldean empire, which (around 3000 BC) was the centre of the Sumerian world

Thebes: a Grecian city that was the home of some of the most famous Greek myths, such as those of Dionysius, Hercules, Oedipus, and Antigone

Babylon: the capital city of the Chaldean empire (see above), whose hanging garden was one of the seven wonders of the ancient world; also the place to which the Jews were brought in captivity by Nebuchadnezzar early in the sixth century BC

Cnossos: an ancient city in the northern part of the Greek island of Crete, home of the world's oldest civilisation, the Minoan

Mycenae: one of the most important early Greek cities, this was the centre of the Mycenaean culture, whose high point was about 1500–1200 BC; two of its kings, Atreus and Agamemnon, figure prominently in Greek legend

Odysseus: a king of ancient Ithaca and a hero of the Trojan Wars, whose ten years of wandering after the war are the subject of Homer's *Odyssey*; called 'Ulysses' by the Romans

Job: an Old Testament figure who heroically remains faithful to God despite being forced to suffer much unjustified pain

Jupiter: in Roman mythology also known as 'Jove', the highest god; the Greeks called him 'Zeus'

Gotama: Siddartha Gautama (560–480 BC), the founder of Buddhism, a highly ascetic Eastern religion that preaches renunciation of the world; also called 'Buddha' ('the enlightened one')

Athens: the capital city of ancient Greece and the site of many famous Greek legends

Rome: the capital city of what is now Italy; in antiquity the empire of the Romans controlled most of the known world

Jerusalem: the capital city of ancient Judea and a city sacred to Jews, Christians and Muslims

Middle Kingdom: the imperial state of Honan in central China during the Chan dynasty

King Lear: one of Shakespeare's greatest tragic heroes

Thoughts of Pascal: a famous book by the influential French religious philosopher, mathematician, and physicist, Blaise Pascal (1623–62)

Passion: the story of Christ's crucifixion; here recounted in a musical setting

Requiem: a musical setting for a Catholic mass for the dead (though here also Protestant masses); from the first word of the psalm verse, *Requiem aeternam dona eis, Domine* ('Grant them eternal rest, O Lord')

symphony: a musical composition written for an orchestra, usually in four parts, or movements

feelies: an advanced form of the 'talkies'—motion picture films with sound-tracks, which were new in 1932; described on pp.136–8 of the novel

the Alhambra: an ornately beautiful thirteenth-century Moorish palace in Granada, Spain, which in the Brave New World has become the name of a feelie theatre; the same name also became frequently used for cinemas in our own time. Huxley's point here is the reduction in futuristic London of great cultural achievements from the past

diaphragms: a diaphragm, in a human being, is a layer of tissue separating the chest area from the abdomen

Synthetic Music Machine: as with blood-surrogate, acetate cloth, the discarnate voice and the vibro-vacuum machines all mentioned above, an indication of the pervasive artificiality of Brave New World existence, in which something living or genuine has been replaced wherever possible with a machine or something machine-made

pegs: bolts to hang clothes on

chypre: a perfume

midden: a dunghill or a garbage-heap

Dr Wells: possibly a reference to H. G. Wells (1866–1946), a highly influential early twentieth-century writer of science fiction and utopian novels whose work stimulated Huxley's. In an interview Huxley said that *Brave New World* 'started out as a parody of H. G. Wells's *Men Like Gods*' (1923); and in a letter written while *Brave New World* was in progress, Huxley wrote 'I am writing a novel about the future—on the horror of the Wellsian utopia and a revolt against it' (to Mrs Kethevan Roberts, 1931)

ovarin: presumably, an artificial substance that, in a human being, would be produced by the female reproductive organs, the ovaries

Mammary Gland: the milk-producing glands of the female

Our Freud: referring to the Viennese psychiatrist Sigmund Freud (1856–1939), another prototype of the Brave New World deity. Huxley felt that Freud oversimplified human psychology by placing too great an emphasis on sexuality; but later in the novel (Chapter 8) Huxley draws upon Freud's theory of the Oedipus Complex in portraying the relationship between the Savage, his mother, Linda, and her lover, Popé. In this theory the son is attracted to the mother and violently jealous of his father (in Huxley's story Popé is a surrogate-father to the Savage). The name of the theory derives from the Greek legend of Oedipus who unknowingly killed his father and married his mother

Samoa: a chain of islands in the Pacific Ocean

New Guinea: a large island north of Australia

Trobriands: a group of coral islands in the Solomon Sea, north of New Guinea

monogamy: marriage to one partner at a time

'Ford's in his flivver ... world': a parody of Browning (see above): 'God's in His heaven—/ All's right with the world' (*Pippa Passes*, 1, 'Morning'). A 'flivver' is a cheap auto-mobile; it is, of course, dubious that there would still be automobiles six hundred years in the future

pneumatic: inflated by compressed air; once again, machine imagery is applied to humans—sexually-desirable females are consistently described in the novel as being 'pneumatic'

Ectogenesis: the creation of structures on the outside of an organism

Pfitzner and Kawaguchi: fictitious scientists who lived at a future time, but before the Brave New World had been fully realised

liberalism: open-mindedness, tolerance, progressive attitudes; these traits disappeared from the Brave New World after the 'Nine Years' War' (see pp.48–53)

'Phosgene ... hydrocyonic acid': deadly chemical agents used in warfare; the Germans used such chemicals during the First World War

open order: in formation, but with wide spaces between the aeroplanes

Kurfurstendamm: a famous street in Berlin

the Eighth Arrondissement: an *arrondissement (French)* is a district of Paris

anthrax: a skin disease of sheep and cattle capable of infecting humans

$CH_3C_6H_2(NO_2)_3$: the chemical formula for trinitro toluene (TNT), an important explosive

$H_g(CNO)_2$:   mercuric fulminate, a substance used for making detonators, activated when struck or heated

'the Nine Years' War and the great economic crash': perhaps meant to parallel significant events of Huxley's own day, the First World War and the economic crash of 1929; hence, the similarity between the evolution of the Brave New World and contemporary history

conscientious objection: a refusal to act, made on moral grounds

viscose fur: another artificial article of clothing

Simple Lifers: presumably, those who wished to return to a more natural, as opposed to an industrial, way of life; see p.49

Golders Green: a green is a grassy common, or public area; Golders Green is a northern suburb of London

British Museum: the national library and museum of Great Britain; its official guide defines its purpose as 'the advancement of learning by the provision of materials and facilities for research, and by the encouragement of the study of literature, history, archaeology and art'; hence, the massacre of the 'culture fans' at the British Museum was the death-knell for intellectual life in the Brave New World

dichlorethyl sulphide: one of the chemical-warfare agents mentioned on p.48; called 'mustard gas' because of its burning effect on the eyes and lungs

morocco-surrogate cartridge belt: a belt holding, here, encased contraceptives and made of imitation morocco, a fine flexible leather

Malthusian: referring to the British economist Thomas Robert Malthus (1766–1834), who urged birth control as a means of regulating population; Huxley believed over-population to be one of the greatest threats to individual liberty—see *Brave New World Revisited*, Chapter 1

black-patent bandolier: a shoulder-belt made of shiny black leather used for holding contraceptive cartridges

opening date of the new era: this hypothetical era is the world's third, 'AF' ('After Ford'); the first two are referred to by the initials 'BC' ('Before Christ') and 'AD' ('Anno Domini'—*(Latin)* 'in the year of our Lord')

fixation of nitrogen: the process of converting atmospheric nitrogen into a solid state

Ford's Day: presumably the Brave New World's substitute for Sunday

morphia and cocaine: narcotic drugs; morphia is derived from the opium poppy, cocaine from the leaf of the coca tree

pharmacologists: those who study drugs. Here begins a brief history of the development of *soma*, the 'perfect drug': 'euphoric, narcotic, pleasantly hallucinant'—that is, *soma* induces a sense of drowsy well-being and produces pleasing illusions; *soma* also lacks negative side-effects (p.53); in *Brave New World*, the drug is used to keep people from thinking or feeling deeply. Huxley later came to believe, through his own experiments, that drugs could provide spiritual insight, as suggested in his last novel, *Island* (1962)

'Hoity-toity': proud, arrogant; Henry Foster is thus accusing Bernard Marx

Gonadal hormones: those chemical compounds produced by the male
and female sex organs
magnesium salts: salts which are used as a purgative

Chapter 4

Late that same afternoon, Lenina takes Bernard up on his earlier
proposal to join him on a holiday at the Savage Reservation in New
Mexico. Lenina then meets Henry Foster and flies off with him for an
evening's entertainment.

At the same time that Lenina and Henry are being entertained,
Bernard calls on Helmholtz Watson, who, like Bernard, feels himself to
be an outsider. Helmholtz reveals to Bernard his frustration at being
unable to realise his latent poetic inspiration.

NOTES AND GLOSSARY:
parathyroid: four small glands attached to, or embedded in, the
thyroid gland, which secrete the hormone para-
thormone (whereas the text implies that parathyroid is a hormone); normally, hyper-secreting
parathormone produces a greatly excited nervous
system—not the over-sized ears Lenina notices on
George Edzel
Charing-T Tower: Charing Cross is the site in London of the last of the
stone crosses Edward I placed in 1291 to mark the
resting points of the funeral procession of his wife,
Queen Eleanor. Today it is a railway station, and a
replica of the original cross still stands at the main
entrance to the station; but in the Brave New World,
a Fordian 'T' tower has replaced the Christian cross
Hampstead: a northern village suburb of London, situated on a
hill
simian: monkey-like
phial: a small glass bottle for medicine
sex-hormone chewing-gum: presumably, chewing-gum that stimulates
the sex organs
an octave and a half: an octave is a musical scale of eight notes
cockchafer: a large type of beetle that makes a loud whirring
sound
stag-beetle: another large beetle, whose mandibles resemble stag
antlers
stays: a supporting tie- or cross-piece in earlier models of
aircraft; again, the technology of AF 632 is dated
planes: aircraft wings

maggoty:	resembling maggots, the wormlike larval form of certain insects, especially flies, that thrive on rotting food. This, along with those in the preceding paragraph, is the first of several references in the novel connecting life in the Brave New World with that of insects—many species of which feed on other forms of life, and which often develop rigidly-regulated societies like that of futuristic London
fore-shortened life:	from the perspective of the helicopter, the people on the ground appear to be shorter than they actually are
Riemann-surface:	a surface consisting of several levels or layers, named for its creator, the German mathematician Georg Friedrich Bernard Riemann (1826–66)
Notting Hill ... Hounslow:	suburbs west of London
hectares:	a hectare is a measure of land which equals 10,000 square metres
revitrifying the surface of the Great West Road:	that is, the men are renewing the glassy surface of the main road westward out of London
Brentford:	a suburb west of London
aphides:	the plural form of aphis, or greenfly, another insect, which attacks plants
mulberry-coloured:	dark reddish-purple, like the mulberry fruit
Stoke Poges:	a village in Buckinghamshire, west of London; it has a famous golf course. Its churchyard is the burial place of the poet Thomas Gray (1716–71); it is also reputedly the setting of his 'Elegy Written in a Country Churchyard' (1751), and some readers think that Huxley is parodying Gray's poem here
lock-up:	here, a rented hangar for aircraft
Fleet Street:	one of the most famous of London's streets; traditionally the location of the major newspaper offices, and so a satirically fitting location for the Brave New World's 'Bureaux of Propaganda'
Exmoor:	a large area of moorland in south-west England

Chapter 5

Lenina and Henry's evening out is presented. After a game of obstacle golf, the couple dine and dance, drug themselves with *soma*, then go to bed.

Again simultaneous, with Lenina and Henry's date, Bernard leaves Helmholtz to go to the required weekly ' Solidarity Service', a substitute religious communion. This ritual is an orgiastic attempt at self-annihilation in which the individual merges with the group. But the deeply dissatisfied Bernard finds no comfort in the service.

NOTES AND GLOSSARY:

Internal and External Secretion Trust: the hormones of, and milk from, cattle are respectively the 'internal' and 'external' secretions referred to here

Farnham Royal: a small village near Stoke Poges

Burnham Beeches: a woodland near Stoke Poges

pullulation: a rapid sprouting or springing up

Slough: an industrial town west of London

phosphorus: one of the elements; Huxley's point here is the desecration of the dead in the Brave New World, funeral rituals being important in most civilisations

P_2O_5: the chemical formula for phosphorus pentoxide, formed when bones are burnt in the air

switchback: a rapid, violent change of direction; Lenina is appropriately appreciative of the physical sensation the switchback produces

Westminster Abbey Cabaret: another desecration, for Westminster Abbey, built in the tenth century, is the site of the coronations of English monarchs and the burial-place of many illustrious dead

ambergris: a substance extracted from whales for use in expensive perfumes

sandalwood: a scent derived from certain Asian trees

'There ain't no Bottle ... of mine': perhaps a loose parody of a popular American song, 'Dear Old Pal of Mine' (1918), which is, however, in four-four time (rather than five-four time, as is the *Brave New World* version); it would have been something of an 'old favourite' even in 1932 because John McCormack (1884–1945), a popular tenor in the decades preceding the publication of *Brave New World*, sang it at all his engagements

the alto and tenor registers: musical pitches; alto is higher than tenor

little death: a traditional label for the sex act, so-called because the feeling of exhaustion after climax is said to resemble a sort of miniature death

harmonies: in music, tones of varied frequencies

A flat major: a musical note half a tone below A

deturgescence: the emptying of something that was tightly full

diminuendo: in music: to become gradually softer

quarter tones: in music, sounds that are one-fourth of a whole step

dominant chord: a group of three or more musical notes, five degrees above the tonic (the note around which a composition is built)

five-four rhythms: musical measures whose beat consists of five quarter-notes

Aphroditaeum: in Greek mythology, Aphrodite was the goddess of sensual love; it is therefore appropriate that Helmholtz Watson, an 'indefatigable lover' (p.62), should be a member of this club. There is, however, some incongruity in Huxley's reference to a figure from ancient mythology in the context of a society where the belief that 'history is bunk' has swept away the past, including that of classical Greece

Fordson Community Singery: a desecration of St Paul's Cathedral, second in importance only to St Peter's in the Vatican; pp.70–1 describe features of St Paul's desecrated in the Brave New World

Carrara-surrogate: Carrara is the world's finest marble, named after the area in Italy where it is mined; again, a thing of great beauty and value has been reduced to artificial form in the Brave New World

Ludgate Hill: the street providing the main approach to St Paul's (the Fordson Community Singery in futuristic London)

Big Henry, the singery clock: presumably, Big Ben has been moved from its site at the Houses of Parliament in Westminster, and been renamed after Henry Ford. In fact 'Big Ben' is the name of the bell that chimes the hours, and not the name of the clock itself

bass: deep-sounding

lout: a coarse-mannered fellow

plangently: with a mournful, moaning sound

midriff: the waist area of the body. Henry is saying that the music affects its listeners on a 'gut' (emotional) level

The dedicated *soma* tablets: these replace the traditional wafers that represent the body of Christ in the Christian Communion sacrament; hence the Brave New World ritual is a blasphemous parody

The loving cup of strawberry ice-cream *soma*: this replaces the consecrated wine, which represents the blood of Christ in the Communion sacrament

galvanic: electric, energetic

descending scale: in music: moving down from high to low notes

solar plexus: the middle of the abdomen; again, the effect suggested is a so-called 'gut-response'

slabbily: a neologism, or newly-coined word, whose sound when pronounced out loud is meant to suggest the slapping of buttocks in the story

'orgy-porgy ... release': the Brave New World version of the nursery rhyme: 'Georgie Porgie, pudding and pie,/ Kissed the girls and made them cry;/ When the boys came out to play,/ Georgie Porgie ran away'

liturgical: relating to the Communion Sacrament—or, in this case, to the Brave New World's blasphemous, secularised version of the Communion

the table and its planetary chairs: the arrangement of the furniture resembles our solar system, which has a central sun and planets moving around it

---

Chapter 6

The conventional Lenina is irritated by Bernard's eccentricities, especially his desire for privacy. On her first date with Bernard, Lenina wishes to go to the usual crowd-filled, noisy places, but Bernard wants to spend a quiet evening alone with her. Eventually Bernard succumbs to Lenina, taking *soma* and going to bed with her. But Bernard is dissatisfied with the superficial ease with which his relationship with Lenina is consummated sexually.

The D.H.C. tells Bernard about his trip, long ago, to the Savage Reservation, then warns Bernard against being eccentric. Feeling suddenly important because he might be exiled, Bernard brags about this possibility to Helmholtz, who looks down on Bernard for his bragging.

Bernard and Lenina fly to New Mexico, where they are told about the Savage Reservation by its warden. From a telephone conversation with Helmholtz, Bernard learns that the D.H.C. plans to exile him to Iceland for his deviations from conventional Brave New World behaviour.

NOTES AND GLOSSARY:

New Mexico: Huxley did not himself visit New Mexico, in south-western USA, until 1937, five years after *Brave New World* was published; in an interview he admitted that 'I had no trouble finding my way around the English part of *Brave New World*, but I had to do an enormous amount of reading up on New Mexico, because I'd never been there. I ... did the best I could to imagine it'

Torquay: a seaside resort town in south-west England

Oxford: famous university city on the Thames, north-west of London

St Andrews: on the east coast of Scotland, St Andrews is the home of the Royal and Ancient Golf Club, founded in 1754, which is the authority on the sport of golf; even sports are desecrated in the Brave New World

Lake District: a region of north-west England noted for its mountains and lakes. Early in the nineteenth century, when the romantic 'Lake Poets' William Wordsworth (1770–1850) and Samuel Taylor Coleridge (1772–1834) were writing their greatest work in this region, the Lake District rivalled London as the literary centre of England. The implication is that Bernard is moved by the same beauties of nature that inspired the poetic drives of Wordsworth and Coleridge (whom Bernard could not, of course, have read)

Skiddaw: the highest mountain in the Lake District

Semi-Demi-Finals: semi- and demi- both mean 'half' or 'partial'; thus, 'Semi-Demi-Finals' would actually mean quarter-finals

'A gramme in time saves nine': a parody of the proverb 'a stitch in time saves nine'; as often in the novel, a familiar aspect of Huxley's own day has been converted by the Brave New World to its own purposes

trembling falsettos: vibrating male voices singing above their normal range; as this is usually done out of bad taste or lack of voice control, it is another indication of the lack of aesthetics in futuristic London

key: here, tone of voice

solecism: a breach of etiquette

'go to the Bottomless Past': that is, 'go to hell'; because religion, and therefore hell, has been outlawed in the Brave New World, the epithet has been changed to refer to the infinite past, a sort of hell to the present-oriented Brave New Worlders

The Blue Pacific Rocket: but the rocket crosses the Atlantic Ocean, not the Pacific

New Orleans: a large city in the state of Louisiana

Santa Fé: the capital city of the state of New Mexico

Aurora Bora: the *aurora borealis*, or 'northern lights', are spectacular, multi-coloured patterns of light sometimes seen in the sky in northern regions of the world

caffeine: a mildly stimulating drug found in coffee and tea; hence, 'boiling caffeine solution' is yet another reference to the artificiality of Brave New World life

an Epsilon-Plus Negro porter: a suggestion that racism still exists, even in AF 632

brachycephalic: in other words, the warden's head was unusually broad in relation to its length

eau-de-Cologne: *(French)* 'water of Cologne', a perfume first manufactured in Cologne, Germany

Grand Canyon: a huge canyon in the state of Arizona

'Those, I repeat, ... there': but John, of course, escapes this destiny

decilitre: one-tenth of a litre

the Director: a slip by Huxley—'The Warden' is meant

half-breeds: a half-breed is a person whose parents are of different races

totemism: a primitive form of religion in which a family or tribe venerates a natural object, usually an animal (as here), as a god-symbol and force of protection; totemism has been outlawed in the Brave New World, whose inhabitants have been conditioned to look upon all religions, as the Warden does here, as 'monstrous superstitions'

Zuñi, Athapascan: Red Indian languages

puma: a big cat found in America

porcupine: a rodent with a spiny coat

stoically: unemotionally accepting one's fate

'Was and will ... am': sleep-teaching slogans important for understanding the Brave New World: its life is lived completely in the present, to which both past and future are considered irrelevant

'Five minutes ... blossomed': the above slogans are realised: the past (roots) and the future (fruits) are replaced by the blossom of the present. Ironically, the imagery implies the impossibility of the very idea it is supposed to convey: without roots, blossoms are impossible; and if they do not bear fruit, blossoms are wasted—thus, the past is necessary for the present to come into existence, and the present is meaningless unless it is directed towards a hopeful future

octoroon: a person who is one-eighth Negro; again, the racism of the Brave New World, in which blacks are relegated to lowly Gamma and Epsilon jobs, is evident

Malpais:	*(Spanish)* 'bad region'
pueblo:	a typical village of the Red Indian tribes of New Mexico; such tribes are known as 'Pueblo' Indians

Taos ... Ojo Caliente: Red Indian and Spanish names of places in New Mexico

---

Chapter 7

Upon entering the Savage Reservation, Lenina and Bernard witness a violent fertility ritual. They meet John Savage, whose white skin has made him an outsider amongst the Indians. Lenina and the Savage are at once attracted to each other. The Savage tells Bernard and Lenina about his mother, Linda, a citizen of the Brave New World who long ago, on a visit to the Reservation while she was pregnant with John, had got lost and had come to live in the Indian community, where John was born. From this story, Bernard deduces that the D.H.C. is the Savage's father. At the Savage's house Bernard and Lenina meet Linda, the first fat and old white person they have ever seen. Lenina is appalled at the sight of Linda and generally dissatisfied with the Indians' primitive ways, in comparison with the civilised ones of the Brave New World.

NOTES AND GLOSSARY:

prow:	the front section of a ship
gunwhale:	the upper edge of the side of a ship
companion ladder:	a ladder leading from the deck of a ship to its cabin
deck:	the floor of a ship
ochre:	a pigment made from ground earth, yellow-brown in colour
'cleanliness is next to fordliness':	a parody of the proverb 'cleanliness is next to godliness'
obsidian:	dark, glassy, volcanic rock
internal secretions:	that is, hormones, which control the growth, development, and functioning of body parts
metabolism:	chemical changes in the body by which food is converted into living tissue (anabolism) and protoplasm into energy (catabolism)
ophthalmia:	inflammation of the eye
treble:	high-pitched
mottled:	spotted
corn:	maize
breech cloth:	a cloth covering only the buttocks and genitals
'Good-morrow':	the savage's English is based on the language of Shakespeare, which is why it sounds 'peculiar' to Bernard and Lenina

'that damned spot': also in reference to blood, Shakespeare's Lady Macbeth exclaims, 'Out, damned spot! out, I say!' (*Macbeth*, V.i.35); the tragic vision with which Shakespeare provides the Savage is a counter to the superficial happiness of the Brave New World, which has eliminated tragedy

'The multitudinous seas incarnadine': again in reference to blood, Macbeth says, 'Will all great Neptune's oceans wash this blood/ Clean from my hand? No; this my hand will rather/ The multitudinous seas incarnadine,/ Making the green one red'. (*Macbeth*, II.ii.57–60)

'They ... complexion': racism also exists in the Indian community

Pookong: a Pueblo village in New Mexico; but here the word is apparently used as the name of an Indian equivalent of Christ

'real silk acetate': Linda's expression here is unintentionally ironic, for (as noted above) acetate is a synthetic material; to people conditioned by Brave New World slogans, the artificial is the real

viscose velveteen: imitation velveteen made, not from cotton, as genuine velveteen is, but from a synthetic material

mescal: a hallucinogenic drink

peyothyl: a hallucinogenic cactus

Chelsea: a royal borough of London, located south-west of the city's centre; although long associated with famous men (the Victorian writer Thomas Carlyle (1795–1881), for example, was known as the Sage of Chelsea), Chelsea has also been associated with the exotic and the scandal-ridden (Oscar Wilde (1856–1900) the playwright condemned for his homosexuality, is one whose name is associated with the region), which is perhaps why in the Brave New World it is made the site of the Abortion Centre; or perhaps because it is one of London's most fashionable residential districts, Chelsea is used ironically here

'Streptocock-Gee ... W.C.': Brave New World version of the nursery rhyme: 'Ride a cock-horse to Banbury Cross,/ To see a fine lady upon a white horse'

embryo poison: that is, alcohol: Lenina identifies the alcohol she smells on Linda's breath with the alcohol she pours, during her work, into bottles containing embryos, to stunt their development in order to produce the lower-caste members of Brave New World society

Chapter 8

Bernard listens as the Savage tells him his life story, which focuses firstly on the oedipal triangle (see note on Our Freud, p.21) of the Savage, his mother Linda, and her lover Popé; and secondly on his acquaintance with Shakespeare's works, from which the Savage makes frequent quotations.

NOTES AND GLOSSARY:

tortillas: round, flat pieces of Indian bread made from corn meal

'Bye, Baby Bunting ... decanting': Brave New World version of the English nursery rhyme lines: 'Bye, baby bunting,/ Daddy's gone a-hunting'

big wooden things with strings fastened to them: that is, looms for handmaking fabrics from cotton and wool; the non-mechanical, non-artificial nature of Indian life contrasts with the mechanical artificiality of the Brave New World

the great Transformer ... Acoma: the Savage mixes references to Pueblo religious mythology with Christian matter (the Spaniards forced Christianity on the Pueblos in the sixteenth century). According to the Zuñi Curriculum Program, Pueblo Zuñi, Zuñi, New Mexico, Huxley's understanding of Indian mythology and language is dubious; some references here are made up, or misspelled to the point of being unidentifiable

kiathla ... tsithl: see above. These and other Indian words used in the novel are made up or misspelled beyond identification

calcium carbonate: chalk

'Nay, but to live ... sty': from Shakespeare's Hamlet, III.iv.91–9; Hamlet's words to his mother in this passage speak so powerfully to the Savage because, like Hamlet, the Savage is deeply attached to his mother; the coincidence that the Savage just happens to open a copy of Shakespeare's works at such an appropriate passage is, of course, strained

A man can smile and smile and be a villain: Hamlet says of Claudius 'That one may smile, and smile, and be a villain!' (Hamlet, I.v.108)

Remorseless, treacherous, lecherous, kindless villain: another of Hamlet's outbursts against Claudius (Hamlet, II.ii.581)

'When he is drunk ... bed': these are appropriate times to kill Claudius, Hamlet decides, and not—as in the scene in which the lines are spoken—while Claudius is kneeling in attempted prayer (*Hamlet*, III.iii.89–90)

kiva: a secret ceremonial pit of the Pueblo Indians

Tomorrow and tomorrow and tomorrow: the third line of Macbeth's famous speech upon his hearing that Lady Macbeth is dead (*Macbeth*, V.v.17–28)

Miranda: the magician Prospero's 'innocent child' (Shakespeare, *The Tempest*, III.iii.72), the pure, virtuous heroine of the play

'O wonder! ... people in it': the Savage's quotation from *The Tempest* (V.i.181–4) is interspersed with his own unintentionally ironic thoughts and a brief dialogue with Bernard. The passage from Shakespeare reads: 'O wonder!/ How many goodly creatures are there here!/ How beauteous mankind is! O brave new world/ That has such people in't!' These are Miranda's words upon witnessing Prospero's reunion of Alonso and his son, Ferdinand, who had thought each other dead; Miranda had not previously seen any other men besides Prospero (*The Tempest*, V.i.181–4)

Chapter 9

While Lenina, overwhelmed by what she has witnessed at the Indian Reservation, takes a *soma* holiday, Bernard initiates a scheme to counter the D.H.C.'s plan to exile him to Iceland. Bernard flies to Santa Fé, where he telephones Mond to ask permission to bring the Savage and Linda with him back to London. Meanwhile, the Savage breaks into the rest-house at the Reservation to worship over the sleeping Lenina.

NOTES AND GLOSSARY:

agave: a cactus plant; its sap is fermented and distilled into mescal (see Chapter 7)

Whitehall: a main street in central London running from Trafalgar Square to Parliament Square and lined with government office buildings; appropriately, the World Controller's Office is located here

electrolytic shave: that is, Bernard is shaved electrically (Huxley is anticipating the electric razor); in electrolysis, chemical decomposition—here, of Bernard's beard—is achieved by means of an electric current

televisor:	an apparatus for transmitting television programmes; but Huxley apparently uses the word here to mean 'television set'
zippi-camiknicks:	cami-knicks are a woman's undergarment for the area from the chest to the thighs; Huxley's Brave New World version is fastened by means of a zipper, which seems to be for Huxley an emblem of mechanised life
zippyjamas:	Brave New World pyjamas, which are also fastened by zippers
'Her eyes . . . is harsh':	Troilus, 'mad/In Cressid's love' (I.i.51–2), is idealising Cressida's beauty in an exaggerated manner that expresses the Savage's attitude toward Lenina; 'her gait': her manner of walking; 'Handlest in they discourse': say; 'seizure': clasp; 'cygnet's down': young swan's soft feathers (Shakespeare's *Troilus and Cressida*, I.i.54–8)
'On the white wonder . . . sin':	now identifying himself and Lenina with Romeo and Juliet, the Savage slightly misquotes Shakespeare to fit Romeo's speech into the syntax of his own thoughts; the passage actually begins: flies 'may seize/On the white wonder', the remaining lines being accurately quoted; 'vestal': chaste, virginal (*Romeo and Juliet*, III.iii.35–9)

Chapter 10

Back in London, Bernard is accused by the D.H.C. of committing crimes against society on the grounds of his unorthodox, non-conformist behaviour. When the D.H.C. announces the sentence of exile to Iceland, Bernard produces the Savage and Linda. Linda exposes the D.H.C. as being the father of the Savage, and the D.H.C. flees in humiliation.

NOTES AND GLOSSARY:

Bloomsbury:	a district of central London; it contains the University of London and the British Museum, gave its name to an early twentieth-century intellectual circle, the Bloomsbury Group, and has long been synonymous with culture and learning—but in the Brave New World, it has ironically become the site of the Central London Hatchery and Conditioning Centre
aeons:	eternities; immeasurable periods of time

dynamos: machines that convert mechanical energy into electrical energy

'like a babe in a bottle': from the late eighteenth- and early nineteenth-century phrase, 'like a babe in the wood', referring to a public offender placed in the stocks or in a pillory; hence, the D.H.C.'s rewording suggests, with unintended irony, the imprisoning nature of Brave New World society

a scatological rather than a pornographic impropriety: a less vulgar, as opposed to a more vulgar, indecency

Chapter 11

Because she stirs no curiosity and even repulses the Brave New Worlders, and because she wishes only to take *soma*, Linda is put on permanent *soma* holiday. The Savage protests, as this means she will live only a month or two longer, but he finally gives in. Made the Savage's legal guardian, Bernard has been instructed to show the primitive savage the technological wonders of the Brave New World. But Bernard misuses his position as the Savage's guardian to advance himself socially and sexually. The Savage visits the weather station at Charing-T Tower (which he finds inferior to the fantasy of Shakespeare); a factory (at which he vomits at the sight of hundreds of identical-twin workers); Eton (whose scientifically-oriented curriculum bewilders him); and another factory (where he watches workers receive their daily *soma* ration).

Huxley intersperses these episodes with another experimental narrative device: Bernard's written commentary on the Savage's reactions to the Brave New World, as read and commented on by Mond, who is irritated by Bernard's pretentious, opinionated style. The chapter concludes with Lenina and the Savage's date at the feelies, whose realistic sensations arose the Savage's sexual desire for Lenina. But, ashamed of his own desires, the Savage abandons the confused and frustrated Lenina.

NOTES AND GLOSSARY:

rejuvenate: make young again

'what our ancestors used to call eternity': again, life in the Brave New World is lived wholly in the present; see pp.50–1, 85, 89–90

'Eternity was in our lips and eyes': Cleopatra's words to Antony about their past ecstasies bear little relationship to the context in which they are quoted in the novel (Shakespeare's *Antony and Cleopatra*, I.iii.35)

patchouli: a heavily-scented perfume made from the plant of the same name

cadged: begged

Resident Meteorologist: the weatherman assigned permanently to Charing-T Tower

Bombay: the capital city of Maharashtra, a state in west India

Dravidian: a dark-skinned race of south India and Ceylon

'Ariel ... forty minutes': actually, it is Puck in Shakespeare's *A Midsummer Night's Dream*, and not Ariel in *The Tempest*, who says: 'I'll put a girdle round the earth/ In forty minutes' (II.ii.75–6)

cold-pressing: the process of flattening without the aid of heat

chucking and turning machines: that is, lathes—machines in which 'chucks' hold pieces of wood in place, as they are cut to the desired shape by being turned against cutting tools

aquiline and ginger gammas: light reddish-brown people with thin, angular bodies; non-Ayran, they are perhaps of tropical descent

Epsilon Senegalese: people from Senegal, on the west coast of Africa; as with the 'Epsilon-Plus Negro porter' (p.87), the Gamma octoroon pilot (p.90), the black Delta cold-pressers (p.130), and the 'aquiline and ginger' lathe-turners (p.130), these non-whites have been assigned to lower-caste stations in the Brave New World

foundry: a factory that produces such basic materials as glass and metal

millimetres: a millimetre (one-thousandth of a metre) is about one-twenty-fifth of an inch

prognathous: protruding

auburn: reddish-brown

flaxen: pale yellow

Eton: Eton College is a prestigious public (that is, private) school near Windsor, west of London, founded in 1440 by King Henry VI to send scholars on to King's College, Cambridge; Huxley himself studied at Eton (1908–11) before near-blindness forced his withdrawal, and later taught there (1917–19); in the Brave New World, Eton has been reduced to little more than an adolescent conditioning centre

'an interesting example ... object': perversely, in the Brave New World conditioned behaviour is considered 'natural' and instinctive behaviour (here, love between a parent and child) unnatural

Lupton's Tower: an impressive early sixteenth-century structure, on the east side of the Eton School Yard, named for Robert Lupton, Provost of Eton from 1504 to 1535. By AF 632 it has become a gleaming fifty-two-storey skyscraper

ferro-concrete: concrete reinforced with steel

vita-glass: glass that allows ultra-violet rays to penetrate it

chrome-steel: an alloy of chromium and steel used in making automobiles; hence, an appropriate material for a statue of Henry Ford

the Provost: the head of Eton College

the Head Mistress: the principal female teacher

elementary relativity: an introductory course in the study of space and time relationships on the premise that such relationships are not absolute, but depend upon (are relative to) subject and object

soprano: the highest range of the female voice

willowily: naturally, like the natural bend of a willow tree

selenium cells: a selenium cell is a type of photo-electric cell—that is, an apparatus for producing electricity by chemical means (in this case, the chemical element is selenium)

the Savoy: a high-class hotel on the Strand in central London

Brentford: a suburb west of London

'What's in those ... caskets?': In Shakespeare's *The Merchant of Venice*, the gold and silver caskets contain scrolls mocking the materialism of the suitors who choose them; but the lead casket contains a picture of Portia, who must marry the suitor who chooses it

Young Women's Fordian Association: the Brave New World equivalent of the Young Women's Christian Association; referred to on p.152 as 'Y.W.F.A.'

Deauville: a resort town on the north coast of France

Cappriccio: a short, lively, 'capricious' piece of music

arpeggios: musical chords whose notes are played, not simultaneously, as is normal with chords, but successively, usually from bottom to top

Gaspard Forster's ... utterance: that is, the 'much more than human' synthetic voice easily moves from the extremely low bass sound reached by the German composer and singer Kaspar Förster (1617–73), who was famous for the low register he could achieve, to a quivering ('trilled') note far above that reached by Lucrezia Agujari (1743–83; Huxley misspells her name), who

	had a voice capable of astonishingly high pitch; **Ducal:** of a duke; **Parma:** in 1770, a duchy (a territory ruled by a duke) in northern Italy; **Mozart:** the great Austrian composer Wolfgang Amadeus Mozart (1756–91), who after hearing Agujari in Parma in 1770 said that her voice had 'an incredibly high pitch'. Huxley's point here is that, like the synthetic voice at the Solidarity Service (p.74), the synthetic voice in this passage is superior to the human voice
stereoscopic:	three-dimensional
erogenous zones:	areas of the body (here, of the face) that when stimulated produce sexual desire

Chapter 12

When the Savage, tired of being used as an ego-booster, refuses to appear at one of Bernard's parties, Bernard is 'deflated'. The Savage prefers to remain upstairs reading *Romeo and Juliet* and contemplating the beauty of Lenina. In a curious shift of scenes, Mond is seen censoring a brilliant paper on biology because its argument includes consideration of the purpose of life. Returning to the main characters, the narrative shows Bernard's jealousy at the immediate friendship that occurs between the Savage and Helmholtz due to their common love of poetry. Helmholtz reveals that he has 'come into conflict with Authority' over a poem he wrote in praise of solitude.

NOTES AND GLOSSARY:

the Arch-Community-Songster of Canterbury:	what the Primate of all England, the Archbishop of Canterbury, has become in the Brave New World
carotene:	the yellow pigment that gives carrots their colour; the eating of 'carotene sandwiches' and 'vitamin A *pâté*' (for which the nutritious part of the food has been extracted) and the drinking of 'champagne-surrogate' are yet further evidence of the artificiality of all elements of Brave New World life
Diocesan-Singery:	a diocese is normally a Church district administered by a bishop
sepulchral:	gloomy, suggestive of a tomb
St Helena:	a volcanic island in the south Atlantic, the place of Napoleon's exile (1815–21)
'Oh, she doth teach ... dear':	Romeo's words upon first seeing Juliet (*Romeo and Juliet*, I.v.44–7)

'Let the bird ... be': the first three lines of Shakespeare's poem 'The
Phoenix and the Turtle' (1601)
'thou shrieking harbinger': from line 5 of 'The Phoenix and the Turtle'
'every fowl of tyrant wing': line 10 of 'The Phoenix and the Turtle'
'defunctive music': from line 14 of 'The Phoenix and the Turtle'
'Property was thus ... together': lines 37–42 of 'The Phoenix and the
Turtle'
'Is there no pity ... lies': *Romeo and Juliet*, II.v.196–201
guffawing: laughing in a loud, vulgar manner

Chapter 13

Depressed by the Savage's lack of attention, Lenina, following her friend
Fanny's advice, decides to attempt to seduce the Savage. He, however, is
repulsed by Lenina's blatant display of sexuality and becomes violent. A
phone call from the hospital informing the Savage of Linda's imminent
death saves Lenina.

NOTES AND GLOSSARY:
'A doctor a day keeps the jim-jams away': the Brave New World
reworking of the proverb, 'An apple a day keeps the
doctor away'; **jim-jams:** *(colloquial)* nervousness or
depression
V.P.S.: the abbreviation for 'Violent Passion Surrogate'
(see p.141)
Mwanza-Mwanza: Mwanza is a port of Tanzania on Lake Victoria in
eastern Africa
trypanosomiasis: the medical term for sleeping sickness
'Oh you so perfect ... best': now the Savage identifies himself and Lenina
with Ferdinand and Miranda, the virtuous young
lovers of *The Tempest*; these are some of
Ferdinand's words of adoration to Miranda
(III.i.46–7)
'some kinds ... undergone': Ferdinand's justification for his use of
manual labour to win Miranda's sympathy (*The
Tempest*, III.i.2–3)
'Outliving beauty's outward ... decays': Troilus's wish (which he
understands to be impossible) that a woman's
(Cressida's) mind would be forever constant to her
lover even though her body must lose its beauty with
time (*Troilus and Cressida*, III.ii.162–3)
'If thou dost ... rite': Prospero's warning to Ferdinand upon betrothing
his daughter, Miranda, to Ferdinand (*The Tempest*,
IV.i.15–17)

Blackamoor: the character in the feelie reminds the Savage of Shakespeare's Moor, Othello

'The murkiest den ... lust': Ferdinand's reply to Prospero's warning (see above) (*The Tempest*, IV.i.25–8)

'For those milk paps ... eyes': milk paps: female breasts; **window bars:** lattice? bodice? the Savage associates the sight of Lenina's breast with the bitter words of the misanthropic Timon on what he thinks to be the deceiving nature of virgins (Shakespeare, *Timon of Athens*, IV.iii.116–17)

'The strongest oaths ... else': another warning by Prospero to Ferdinand (*The Tempest*, IV.i.52–4)

'Impudent strumpet!': so Othello mistakenly accuses Desdemona (Shakespeare, *Othello*, IV.ii.81)

'The wren ... sight': Lear speaks these lines in bitter disillusionment (Shakespeare, *King Lear*, IV.vi.112–113)

'The fitchew ... imagination': distressed at his daughters' mistreatment of him, Lear rages against the sexual nature of women; **fitchew:** polecat; **Down from the waist they are centaurs:** that is, beasts—in Greek mythology, centaurs had the upper bodies of humans and the lower bodies of horses; **But to the girdle do the gods inherit:** that is, women resemble the gods only in that portion of their bodies above the sexual organs; **civet:** a type of perfume (*King Lear*, IV.vi.122–31)

'O thou weed ... it ...': a conflation of Othello's accusations of adultery to Desdemona (*Othello*, IV.ii.67–77)

'The devil Luxury ... finger': spoken (in prose, rather than in blank verse) in delight by the vulgar Thersites as he, Troilus, and Ulysses secretly witness Cressida's sexual infidelity; **Luxury:** lechery; **potato finger:** finger inviting eroticism (potatoes were believed to be aphrodisiac) (*Troilus and Cressida*, V.ii.55–6)

parleying: discussing

'If I do not usurp myself, I am': Olivia's comic response to the question, 'Are you the lady of the house?'; **usurp myself:** seize power from myself; thus, the Savage has just been asked by the caller if he is the 'man of the house'; his abrupt shift from sour cynicism to comedy is questionable (Shakespeare, *Twelfth Night*, I.v.186)

Park Lane: a thoroughfare in the Mayfair area of central London

Chapter 14

The Savage goes to Linda's bedside at the Park Lane Hospital for the Dying. There in a *soma* trance Linda, dreaming of Popé, is unable to recognise her son. Shaking her violently, the Savage finally succeeds in forcing his mother to recognise him, but Linda chokes and dies. During this action, children being 'death-conditioned' intrude rudely upon the Savage's vigil.

NOTES AND GLOSSARY:

moribund:	dying
Super-Vox Wurlitziana:	based upon the 'mighty Wurlitzer' organ used in cinemas in the 1930s
puggishly:	in the manner of a pug dog, a small, flat-faced animal with wide nostrils that resembles a miniature bulldog
taut-skinned:	having tightly-drawn, wrinkle-free skin
sexagenarians:	people aged between sixty and seventy years; in the Brave New World people retain their youth, by artificial means, until they are sixty, at which age they die rapidly
flaccid:	flabby, wrinkled
truculently:	fiercely, aggressively
caffeine solution:	Brave New World coffee and tea substitute (and another artificial foodstuff)
crescendo:	in music, a gradual increase in volume; hence the musical opposite of *diminuendo* (p.69)
ordure:	dung

Chapter 15

As the Savage leaves the hospital, he sees *soma*—which caused the premature death of his mother—being passed out to a large group of workers. Horrified, the Savage now re-interprets Miranda's 'brave new world' speech as heralding his own mission to save the workers from the dangers of *soma*. While the Savage is urging the workers to rebel, Helmholtz arrives at the scene with Bernard, and the Savage by this time is throwing handfuls of *soma* tablets out of the window. But this only incites the workers to attack the Savage, to whose defence Helmholtz rushes, whilst Bernard is humiliatingly unable to decide what to do. Finally, the police arrive and, with the aid of *soma* spray, anaesthetic-squirting pistols, and 'Synthetic Anti-Riot Speech Number Two (Medium Strength)', quell the riot. The Savage, Helmholtz, and Bernard are led away under arrest.

NOTES AND GLOSSARY:

dolichocephalic: long-headed

'Lend me your ears': the Savage addresses the crowd in the manner he knows best, by recalling an appropriate line from Shakespeare—here, he is remembering the first line of Mark Antony's famous speech in *Julius Caesar* that begins, 'Friends, Romans, countrymen, lend me your ears!' (III.ii.73)

propitiatingly: in a pacifying manner

Biarritz: a resort on the south-west coast of France

'Ford in Flivver!': 'God in Heaven!'—'Ford' is, of course, early in the novel established as the Brave New World analogue for 'God', and 'flivver' has earlier been made analogous with 'heaven' by way of a parody of Browning (p.45)

mewling: whimpering

carapace: the shell of a tortoise or a crustacean

'Ford helps those who help themselves': Brave New World alteration of a proverb from Benjamin Franklin's *Poor Richard's Almanack* (1733), 'God helps them that help themselves'

anaesthetic: here, a drug that knocks its recipient out

wambling: a neologism meaning wobbily, unsteady

Bursary: as a bursary is normally a treasury, the suggestion is that in the Brave New World *soma* is equivalent to money

baritone valedictons: words of farewell delivered in a male voice of middle range

'Will you come ... anaesthetise?': this replaces the conventional 'Will you come quietly, or must we use force?'; in the Brave New World, the masses are controlled not by force—as in, say, George Orwell's *Nineteen Eighty-Four* (1949)—but by drugs (see p.49)

Chapter 16

In the philosophical climax of the novel, Bernard, the Savage, and Helmholtz are confronted in the World Controller's study by Mond, who preaches Brave New World dogma to them. When Bernard realises that he is to be exiled, he breaks down and is led out of the room. Mond continues his lecture. Helmholtz chooses as his place of exile a location with a cold climate because he thinks it will stimulate his intellectual work better than a warm location, then leaves the room to look after Bernard.

NOTES AND GLOSSARY:

bobbins: usually, wooden sticks holding thread; here, cylinders around which reading material is wound

Detroit: a large city in the state of Michigan, USA, and the home base of the American motor industry; Henry Ford was born and died just outside the city

'Sometimes a thousand ... voices': Caliban is telling Stephano about the delightful exotic sounds of the island on which he lives (*The Tempest*, II.ii.137–38); the Savage's verbatim memory of often lengthy and obscure, but appropriate, passages is strained enough—but when Mond, too, begins quoting Shakespeare word-for-word, the device perhaps begins to parody itself

'Goats and monkeys!': animals, conventionally considered lecherous, referred to by Iago ('as prime as goats, as hot as monkeys') when he is trying to convince Othello of Desdemona's unfaithfulness (*Othello*, II.ii.403)

'told by an idiot': according to Macbeth, life: 'is a tale/ Told by an idiot, full of sound and fury,/ Signifying nothing.' (*Macbeth*, V.v.26–8)

gyroscope: an instrument used to stabilise ships and aircraft; it has a wheel mounted in such a way that it is free to rotate on any axis; the conventional 'ship of state' metaphor has been modernised to 'rocketship of state'

Cyprus: a British Crown Colony at the time *Brave New World* was written, this island is in the extreme eastern part of the Mediterranean Sea, south of Turkey

scullion: literally, a boy dish-washer, but used metaphorically by Mond here

matriarchies: a matriarchy is a society organised with the mother as head and with inheritance passed down through the female line of the family

Marquesas: a group of Polynesian islands in the South Pacific

Samoa: another group of South Pacific Polynesian islands

Falkland Islands: rocky, barren islands with a cool climate in the south Atlantic, off the southern coast of Argentina

Chapter 17

Mond and the Savage, now alone, debate religion. Mond explains at some length the Brave New World 'religion' of social stability produced by freely-expressed sensuality and happiness without pain. But the Savage rejects this religion, preferring instead a more dangerous but more moral world.

NOTES AND GLOSSARY:

The Imitation of Christ: a famous book (1427) by the German Christian mystic Thomas à Kempis (*c.*1380–1471), arguing that to achieve divine grace one must imitate the great suffering and self-sacrifice of Christ

The Varieties of Religious Experience: the principal work (1902) of the American philosopher and psychologist William James (1842–1910), the novelist Henry James's older brother; this popular, influential book argues the practicality of enacting a form of conduct that is based upon religious principles

Cardinal Newman: John Henry Newman (1801–90), a prominent Victorian writer, educator, and religious thinker

'I, Pandulph, of fair Milan cardinal': from Shakespeare's *King John*, III.i.138

Maine de Biran: a minor French philosopher (1766–1824) whose mysticism was a reaction against contemporary rationality; Huxley became more attracted to Biran's ideas toward the end of his life, when his own thinking was moving toward mysticism, and wrote a lengthy essay on Biran, 'Variations on a Philosopher', published in *Themes and Variations* (1950)

'A man ... earth': a paraphrase of Hamlet's words to the awestruck Horatio as he and Hamlet are confronted by the ghost of Hamlet's father: 'There are more things in heaven and earth, Horatio,/ Than are dreamt of in your philsophy.' (*Hamlet*, I.v.166–7)

Bradley: Francis Herbert Bradley (1846–1924), a British idealist philosopher

'The gods ... eyes': Edgar's words to his half-brother Edmund, the bastard son of Gloucester (who is also Edgar's father); the 'pleasant vice' of adultery has 'plagued' Gloucester in that its product, Edmund, was the 'instrument' that 'cost him his eyes'; **'The dark and vicious place where he got thee':** the genitals of Edmund's mother (*Lear*, V.iii.171–4)

'Thou hast spoken ... here': The wheel: the wheel of fortune; **I am here:** that is, near darkness, the state one is in both before birth and after death (*Lear*, V.iii.174–5)

'But value dwells ... prizer': that is, things are intrinsically valuable, besides the value an individual (the 'particular will' of 'the prizer') attaches to them (see Shakespeare's *Troilus and Cressida*, II.ii.53–6)

neurasthenia: weakness of nerves

'if after ... death': Othello's joyful words upon being reunited with Desdemona (*Othello*, II.i.185–6)

Mátsaki: a Pueblo village, no longer in existence

'Whether 'tis nobler ... them': these lines immediately follow the words 'To be or not to be, that is the question' in Hamlet's famous soliloquy; slings: a sling is an old-fashioned weapon for hurling stones (*Hamlet*, III.i.56–9); the Savage's own choice, of course, will be 'not to be' — that is, suicide

'Exposing what ... egg-shell': see *Hamlet*, IV.iv.51–3

adrenals: two glands, lying in the area of the kidneys, that secrete adrenalin, a stimulating hormone that can produce violent action

adrenin: that is, adrenalin

Desdemona: Othello's wife in Shakespeare's play *Othello*, whom he tragically murders because he mistakenly believes her to be sexually unfaithful

syphilis: a disease transmitted by sexual contact

lousy: infested with lice, blood-sucking insects

typhoid: an infectious disease producing a dangerously high fever

Chapter 18

Not allowed to go into exile (as Bernard and Helmholtz are) because Mond wishes to experiment with him, the Savage flees London for the primitive English countryside. He is initially happy in his solitude, but then recalls that he has dedicated his life to punishing himself for his 'murderous unkindness' to Linda. Curiosity-seekers from the civilised world invade his privacy, eventually luring him into a violent orgy. Next day, when he realises what he has done, the Savage feels so guilty that he hangs himself.

NOTES AND GLOSSARY:

Guildford ... Portsmouth: towns between London and the English Channel

the guilty Claudius: Claudius, who has obtained the throne by murdering Hamlet's father, tries in vain to ask heaven's forgiveness for his evil deed (*Hamlet*, III.iii.36–98)

silos: towers for storing grain

vitamin D factory: to the very end of the story, Huxley continues to emphasise the artificiality of Brave New World life

fire drill: a primitive device for starting a fire of the sort the Savage would have used at the Indian Reservation; the device simply consists of a stick that is turned rapidly on a piece of wood until the resulting friction produces fire

pan-glandular: **pan:** all; **glandular:** referring to the glands, organs that secrete chemicals essential to bodily functions; hence, 'pan-glandular biscuits' are a food containing a synthetically-manufactured supply of all the chemicals produced by the body's glands

copse: a coppice, a small wood consisting of small trees that are cut periodically

nocked: that is, the Savage has made a notch on the end of each arrow to receive the bow-string of his weapon

a stethoscopic wheeze: a sound similar to what a medical doctor would hear through a stethoscope while listening to a sick patient's lungs

foot-and-mouth-baller: presumably, a Brave New World football, or soccer, player

coccyx: the small, triangular bone at the base of the spine; here, a satirically polite euphemism for 'bottom'

SENSATION IN SURREY: Surrey is the county south of London in which this action takes place; the use of overstatement and alliteration, as well as the meaninglessness of the phrase, are a satire on the news media's sensationalistic 'yellow journalism'; Huxley was himself a professional journalist for a good part of his career

Four-Dimensional Continuum: the three known dimensions are length, breadth, and thickness or depth; the fourth dimension is often considered to be time; a 'continuum' is a continuous sequence of related parts

The Fordian Science Monitor: more journalistic satire: a parody of the American newspaper *The Christian Science Monitor*, founded in 1908 by Mary Baker Eddy (1821–1910); she also founded the highly idealistic religion of Christian Science which believes in, for example, faith-healing in the place of medical treatment; the parallel between this sort of religion and Fordianism is perhaps meant as a comment on Brave New World religion

benighted: ignorant, stupid; literally, 'overtaken by night'

supercharger: a device that increases the efficiency of an internal combustion engine by supplying extra petrol or air at a higher-than-normal pressure

winged vermin: a destructive or harmful bird

eternity was in our lips and eyes: Cleopatra's remembrance of her past bliss with Antony now means something different to the Savage from what it meant earlier (see p.127)

telescopic cameras: photographic cameras equipped with special lenses that give an enlarged picture of distant objects

and all our yesterdays ... death: the Savage's meditation on death recalls to him associated references to death in Shakespeare's great tragedies; here, the reference (the novel's third) is to Macbeth's famous speech upon Lady Macbeth's death (*Macbeth*, V.v.22–3)

as flies ... sport: so the dejected Gloucester tells his faithful son, Edgar (*Lear*, IV.i.36–7)

ever-gentle gods: *Lear*, IV.vi.217

thy best of rest ... sleep: see Shakespeare's *Measure for Measure*, III.i.17–19

sleep, perchance to dream: 'To die, to sleep—/ To sleep, perchance to dream ...'. Hamlet's famous soliloquy on death concludes that death may be a state of nightmarish dreams (*Hamlet*, III.i.63–4)

For in that sleep of death, what dreams ...?: *Hamlet*, III.i.65

shantung: a plain, unornamented type of Chinese silk

petits beurres: plain biscuits; literally, 'little butters' *(French)*

babel: a noisy assembly making meaningless sounds

'Fry, lechery, fry!': the Savage recalls Thersites' words, spoken as Thersites, Troilus, and Ulysses watch the seduction scene between Diomedes and Cressida, who has sworn eternal love to Troilus (*Troilus and Cressida*, V.ii.56–7); earlier (p.158), when Lenina had attempted to seduce him, the Savage had recalled the words of Thersites that immediately precede the words he now recalls; thus, the Savage seems to have fixed permanently in his mind a picture of Lenina as a 'strumpet', as he calls her both here and in the earlier episode, to the exclusion of considering the genuine love Lenina feels for him—the Savage is, in his own way, as unsatisfactory as the Brave New Worlders he cannot himself tolerate

six-eight time: in music, a time signature indicating six eighth-notes per measure; six-eight time is common to marches, which makes it appropriate in this context

Part 3

Commentary

The genre of *Brave New World*

Utopia and dystopia

Brave New World is considered a part of the utopian tradition of literature. The word 'utopia' derives from two related Greek words meaning 'no place' and 'good place'. Conventionally utopian literature portrays an ideal community which the reader is invited to contrast with his own. Although Sir Thomas More (1478–1535) coined the term for his famous *Utopia* (1516), the idea of presenting a perfect world goes back to antiquity, to such myths as the Garden of Eden and such works as Plato's *Republic*. The ideal state pictured in a utopian work may, like More's, exist in the present but be removed geographically from the 'real world' to some imagined place (usually an island); or it may, like Huxley's London in *Brave New World*, be removed in time, to some future date.

However, the presentation of the utopian world may be ironic. That is, what certain characters in a work hold up as being the ideal may be exposed in the end as being quite the opposite. Certain utopian works, in other words, actually present negative, anti-utopias, or 'dystopias' (from the Greek word meaning 'bad place'). *Brave New World* is, clearly, an example of a dystopia.

Science fiction

Often, though not always, utopian works contain a strong element of science fiction, a mode of literature whose setting and action (and, in the case of *Brave New World*, much of its characterisation and some of its language) depend upon scientific technology that is, perhaps, possible, but not as yet realised. The reason for this frequent link between utopianism and science fiction is that because utopias do not, of course, exist in the real world, they lend themselves readily to the sort of speculative fantasy inherent in science fiction. *Brave New World*, for example, is set six hundred years into the future to allow Huxley's scientifically-oriented mind (as noted in Part 1, Huxley initially intended to become a medical doctor) great scope within which to hypothesise such possible technological wonders as test-tube babies, feelies, and sleep-teaching. Aesthetically, the pitfall of science fiction writing is that it can become so absorbed in the conjectured scientific technology it is presenting that it neglects the deeper human questions probed by significant literature. In other words, the scientific machinery can become an end in itself that is paraded before the reader for the sake of its own ingenuity, rather than be a means by which the author grapples with the central problems of existence. This is a significant point in considering the artistic merit of *Brave New World*, for the novel's ultimate aim is not simply to dream about potential scientific marvels, but to comment upon the human condition and to serve warning of what it might possibly become.

Satire

'Satire' is a wide-ranging term that includes literary ridicule. An idea, a person, an action, even the entire human race may be the object of satire. However, the aim of satire is not merely punitive, as for example are blatant sarcasm (bitter irony) and invective (name-calling). Rather, satire seeks, often in a quite subtle manner, to correct the folly, vice, or frailty that it ridicules; it punishes in order to heal. In tone satire may be either lightly amused and comic, or severely bitter and indignant.

The focus of the satire in *Brave New World* is two-directional: first on scientific technology, and second on the related evil of the materialistic, over-regulated, mind- and spirit-numbing society such technology can produce. Huxley is warning that carried to its extreme, science will control man, rather than man control it. Indeed, in *Brave New World* man himself is no longer the product of human sexual relations, but has become the scientifically-calculated, socially-predestined result of test-tube breeding. On the whole, apart from the story's tragic ending, Huxley's mood is light and amused as he pokes fun at the evils he is exposing, especially in the opening three chapters. But, because he is a satirist, Huxley means to do more than to ridicule: he wishes to force the reader to see the possible evils latent in science, which is playing an increasingly dominant role in human life. And furthermore, Huxley wishes to offer an alternative—a world centred upon humanity rather than science, with all the risks, uncertainties, and even pain that such a world entails. 'I don't want comfort,' the Savage argues. 'I want God, I want poetry, I want real dangers, I want freedom, I want goodness. I want sin'. A central question to ask regarding the satire of *Brave New World* is whether its tone is not *too* light; that is, does Huxley undercut his serious purpose by making futuristic London so comical that it is difficult to take seriously the evils he sees in advanced technology?

In sum, then, *Brave New World* can be labelled a satiric science fiction dystopia.

A novel of ideas

Critics generally agree that much of Huxley's fiction is didactic in nature: that is, in his imaginative work Huxley is above all else concerned with propounding, or even propagandising for, various philosophies of religion, politics, society, and art. For Huxley, then, the *idea*, or theme, around which a particular work revolves is of greater importance than plot, character, setting, or language. Such a work is usually termed a 'novel of ideas', or a 'thesis novel', and *Brave New World* can be considered from the perspective of this category. Indeed, Huxley's Foreword to *Brave New World* suggests a didactic intention: unless humanity chooses 'to decentralise and to use applied science, not as the end to which human beings are to be made the means, but as the means to producing a race of free individuals', then humanity risks 'developing, under the need for efficiency and stability, into the welfare tyranny of Utopia' (p.14). Once in the Foreword and four times in *Brave New World Revisited*, Huxley refers to *Brave New World* as a fable—a narrative with an overt moral purpose.

Certainly his own statements about art support the contention that Huxley—who published more than twenty books of non-fiction—is an essay novelist, a novelist of ideas. In a well-known passage from *Point Counter Point* (1928), for instance, Philip Quarles, who is usually considered to be a persona of the author, writes: 'Novel of ideas. The character of each personage must be implied, as far as possible, in the ideas of which he is the mouthpiece.' The life-blood of the novel of ideas is not, then, in the characters or action, but in the ideas themselves; plot and characterisation function primarily to embody and dramatise ideas. And Huxley conceded in an interview that he was not 'a congenital novelist' (in other words, not a born writer of fiction), but a novelist who has 'great difficulty in inventing plots' and who is 'not very good at creating characters'. Instead, he strives to present 'general abstract ideas in terms of concrete characters and situations'. Not only works of art, novels are also 'vehicles for the expression of general philosophic ideas, religious ideas, social ideas'.

The most obvious episodes that shape *Brave New World* into a novel of ideas are those at the beginning and at the end of the narrative. The first two chapters, and most of the third, are presented largely in lecture format, with first the D.H.C. and then Henry Foster actually lecturing to students, who diligently and precisely take down notes of what is said, about the technology of the Brave New World. Then Mustapha Mond, the World Controller, appears to lecture the students on contemporary theories of sexuality, communal living, social stability, and history, and even give a brief lecture on the evolution of the Brave New World. Chapter 16 brings Bernard, Helmholtz, and the Savage before Mond, who again breaks into a lecture (punctuated by questions from his audience) upon the need for individual conformity and social stability. In the next chapter, the Savage and Mond challenge each other in the sort of debate-lecture format mentioned in Part 1.

In evaluating *Brave New World* (and, indeed, any novel of ideas), the reader would do well to consider the following possible weaknesses of such works:

(1) Are the ideas adequately embodied in the characters and action? That is, given that the novel's ideas are dominant, are these ideas integrated with characterisation and plot well enough to bring the ideas to life? Or do the ideas dominate to the extent that the characters themselves do not seem real or the action significant?

(2) Is there a sufficient clash of ideas to generate dramatic interest? That is, are enough conflicting points of view on a particular issue expressed to provide the sense of drama usually provided by characterisation and plot? Or does the novel offer, instead, a sustained lecture on a single overly-dominant idea or set of ideas?

(3) Are the ideas themselves stimulating enough to sustain novel-length treatment? Or do they seem dated or simply too feeble to hold the reader's interest for any length of time?

The novel's language

'All literature,' Huxley has written, 'is a mixture in various proportions, of magic and science.' These two linguistic extremes, the magical and the scientific, form a basic contrast in the language of *Brave New World*. The magical element in the novel is provided mainly by *(a)* Helmholtz Watson's poetic drive and *(b)* references to Shakespeare.

Helmholtz represents the artistic inspiration suppressed by the Brave New World. Helmholtz lectures for the College of Emotional Engineering, writes for the radio and the feelies, and possesses 'the happiest knack for slogans and hypnopaedic rhymes' (p.62). Yet these non-aesthetic uses of his capacity for language only seem to make him aware that his poetic impulse, his 'extra, latent power', is frustrated (p.147; see also p.43). He feels he has 'something else' to communicate (pp.62, 64, 147) far more significant than Brave New World propaganda. He sums up his own plight: 'I've got something important to say and the power to say it—only I don't know what it is, and I can't make any use of the power. If there was some different way of writing ... Or something else to write about ...' (p.64; Huxley's ellipses). And when Helmholtz is able to express himself in poetic form, his subject, the forbidden one of solitude, only brings him 'into conflict with Authority' (p.146). In reaction to the mind-numbing effect of Brave New World doggerel, Helmholtz seeks a 'more intense, more violent' language (p.64) based upon 'penetrating, X-rayish phrases' (p.149; see also p.64). Indeed, he believes that only 'madness and violence' (p.150), and not the overly-sane stability of the Brave New World, can produce such a poetic language: Shakespeare was great 'Because he had so many insane, excruciating things to get excited about. You've got to be hurt and upset' to write genuine poetry (p.149). Hence, his choice for a place of exile is the Falkland Islands because 'I believe one would write better if the climate were bad. If there were a lot of wind and storms, for example' (pp.183–4).

Besides the purposes discussed below, the Shakespeare theme also develops the linguistic opposition between 'magic and science'. For the Savage finds Shakespeare's words 'singing and magic' (p.111), more magical even than those contained in the Indian rituals he was brought up with. Shakespeare speaks to the Savage with 'a terrible beautiful magic' (p.110) in words whose 'magic was strong' enough to make his own feelings 'real' (p.111). Finally, emphasis on the magical quality of Shakespeare's poetry is keynoted by the novel's allusion in the title to *The Tempest*, whose central character, Prospero, is a magician.

The other extreme of language to Huxley, the scientific, is rendered in *Brave New World* in several modes: *(a)* pseudo-poetry; *(b)* parody; *(c)* lecture; *(d)* synthetic voice; *(e)* a plain prose style. These modes are 'scientific' in that either they are products of technology (for example, the synthetic voice), or they are the results of technology's influence (for example, parody is often used to show how science has drained the life-blood out of the arts). Inevitably, some of these modes overlap.

Pseudo-poetry is, of course, not really poetry at all. Written in verse form (that is, in rhyme and metre), it does have on the surface the appearance of poetry, but it lacks the deeper significance of true poetry. The most obvious example of pseudo-poetry in *Brave New World* is the sleep-teaching slogans that are repeated throughout the story: 'A gramme is better than a damn'; 'ending is better than mending'; 'Was and will make me ill'. Such doggerel serves at least three purposes: it adds to the novel's comic texture; it provides, in concise and memorable fashion, key tenets of Brave New World philosophy; it exposes the lack of aesthetic richness in the Brave New World by providing a contrast with the splendid poetry quoted from Shakespeare.

A second anti-magical use of language in the novel involves parody, the imitation by one work of another work for purposes of ridicule. Normally, the ridicule is aimed at the work that is imitated; but Huxley aims his ridicule at the Brave New World, the imitator. When lines of poetry are parodied, the parody becomes a form of pseudo-poetry, for instance, the parody of Browning: 'Ford's in his flivver; All's well with the World' (p.45). Huxley is here comically showing the reduction to triviality in the Brave New World of once-significant art. Again combining pseudo-poetry and parody, Huxley also mimics several nursery rhymes, most notably in connection with the 'Orgy-Porgy' ritual of sensuality (pp.75, 205). The implication of such parodies is that the Brave New World is, spiritually, a nursery school for adults whose pupils can be motivated by appropriate rhymes. Another recurring type of parody is that of everyday, casual references to God, who becomes in the Brave New World 'Our Ford—or Our Freud' (p.41). Thus, characters frequently exclaim, 'Oh, Ford!' or some variant, or, even parodying Benjamin Franklin unawares, 'Ford helps those who help themselves' (p.171). Again, comic reduction is Huxley's point. The novel also employs non-linguistic forms of parody. For example, the Christian gesture of making a cross over the heart is replaced in the Brave New World by the making of a 'T', in reverence to 'Our Ford', over the stomach (p.31); and the Solidarity Service (pp.72–3) is a parody of the Christian Communion.

The use of the lecture technique in *Brave New World* has already been mentioned. The language this technique requires is more rhetorical—more formal and more tightly organised—than casual speech. The D.H.C., for example, begins his lecture to the students with a formal introduction: 'I shall begin at the beginning' (p.16). He proceeds to develop his subject by use of technical and scientific terminology, some of it drawn from the vocabulary of the real world (ova, male gametes), some of it fabricated by the author to provide a sense of scientific advancement appropriate to the year AF 632 (bokanovskify, Podsnap's Process). A representative passage will demonstrate these characteristics: '"Essentially," the D.H.C. concluded, "bokanovskification consists of a series of arrests of development. We check the normal growth and, paradoxically enough, the egg responds by budding"' (p.17). Mustapha Mond's words are, likewise, generally closer to those of a formal lecture than they are to everyday speech. Mond delivers lengthy, carefully-organised set pieces, one after another, to his audience, occasionally drawing upon literary quotations to round off his points. His lectures are also presented in balanced, rhetorical periods:

> 'And why should we go hunting for a substitute for youthful desires, when youthful desires never fail? A substitute for distractions, when we go on enjoying all the old fooleries to the very last? What need have we of repose when our minds and bodies continue to delight in activity? of consolation, when we have *soma*? of something immovable, when there is the social order?' (p.187)

The use of the lecture method by those in power in the Brave New World indicates that these leaders have an absolute, unquestioned authority that they presume will be respected (a student who asks a reasonable but potentially embarrassing question is immediately labelled an 'Ass!' by the D.H.C. [p.23]). Moreover, the prominence of the lecture device implies that the Brave New Worlders, unable to think for themselves, turn to authority-figures for answers to their questions (the students' slavish taking of notes at the start of the novel is mocked by Huxley).

Most significant about the occurrence in the novel of the 'Synthetic Voice' is that it is considered to be superior to that of human beings. The bass Synthetic Voice at the Solidarity Service is 'more musical than any merely human voice, richer, warmer, more vibrant with love and yearning and compassion, a wonderful, mysterious, supernatural voice' (p.74). And 'The Voice of Reason, the Voice of Good Feeling' produced by the 'Synthetic Music Box' speaks in a baritone 'straight from the depths of a non-existent heart' (pp.172–3). Indeed, the Synthetic Voice represents an ideal for human speakers to attempt to come up to: 'Mustapha Mond's oratory was almost up to synthetic standards' (p.178). Most frighteningly, the Brave New Worlders respond to the Synthetic Voice more powerfully than they do to the human voice. When the Synthetic Voice at the Solidarity Service speaks, 'A sensation of warmth radiated thrillingly out from the solar plexus to every extremity of the bodies of those who listened; tears came into their eyes; their hearts, their bowels seemed to move within them, as though with an independent life' (p.74). And the Synthetic Voice's 'Anti-Riot Speech Number Two (Medium Strength)' proves so effective 'that, behind their gas-masks, even the policemen's eyes were momentarily dimmed with tears' (p.173).

Finally, the descriptions of futuristic London are rendered in a plain style well suited to the drabness and lack of beauty in the Brave New World. The novel's opening paragraph exemplifies this style:

> 'A squat grey building of only thirty-four stories. Over the main entrance the words, CENTRAL LONDON HATCHERY AND CONDITIONING CENTRE, and, in a shield, the World State's motto, COMMUNITY, IDENTITY, STABILITY.' (p.15)

The diction is simple, the syntax is reduced, like a telegraph's, to only essential constructions, and the imagery is unadorned. This is a 'grey' world, 'cold', the next paragraph says, 'for all the summer beyond the panes' (p.15), a world in which glass and concrete structures overwhelm the individual human being.

The use of Shakespeare

The significance of Shakespeare to *Brave New World* is most evident from the novel's title. Borrowed from *The Tempest* (1611), the phrase 'brave new world' is spoken three times by the Savage. The Savage first utters the words in unintended irony when he thinks rapturously of

Lenina after falling in love with her at first sight (p.116). In Shakespeare's play, Miranda speaks these words in innocent awe at the sudden appearance of several visitors on the apparently uninhabited island on which she lives; their presence is the work of her father's magic. When the Savage quotes Miranda's words, however, he is wondering how many beautiful creatures besides Lenina London contains and is anxious to 'start at once' for that city. Bernard immediately undercuts the Savage's naive optimism: 'hadn't you better wait till you actually see the new world?' And, indeed, the Savage is not long in London before his quotation of Miranda comes back to haunt him: upon seeing numerous groups that each consist of scores of identical-twin workers, the Savage now sees that a 'brave new world that has such people in it' is another from what he had expected (p.131). But when, towards the end, the Savage reinterprets Miranda's words to mean 'the possibility of loveliness, the possibility of transforming even the nightmare into something fine and noble' (p.169), he is again being naive, for the rebellion he attempts to incite excites no followers and leads only to his own arrest and, finally, suicide.

From the moment he is introduced into the narrative (p.98), the Savage continually calls upon Shakespeare to articulate his own thoughts and feelings. Although the novel's title is taken from a late Shakespearean fantasy, the Savage's most frequent quotations are tragical in nature. When he first appears, for example, the Savage expresses his frustration at not being allowed to participate in the fertility dance that has just concluded by using Lady Macbeth's words to refer to the pool of blood left by the ritual's sacrificial victim as a 'damned spot' (p.98). The Savage can best express his reaction to the obscenity of the feelies with another quote from Shakespeare, for 'Only in Othello's words could he find an adequate vehicle for his contempt and hatred' (p.176). When he thinks of Lenina, the Savage invariably recalls passages from *Romeo and Juliet*, Shakespeare's romantic tragedy about star-crossed lovers. For instance, when the Savage observes Lenina sleeping in the rest-house of the Indian Reservation, he immediately thinks of appropriate lines from *Romeo and Juliet* to elucidate his own worship of Lenina (pp.119–20). The function of these allusions to Shakespeare's tragedies is made explicit by Mond: 'You can't make tragedies without social instability. The world's stable now' (p.177). The artificial happiness and stability of the Brave New World, in other words, have eliminated the occurrence of tragical situations; whereas, as the Savage argues, there must be the possibility of genuine pain and danger if human life is to have any meaning (p.192).

Besides providing the novel with its ironic title and the central contrast between contrived, superficial happiness and the tragedy that is necessary to a fulfilling life, Huxley's use of Shakespeare also suggests one of *Brave New World's* main themes. For, taken all together, the references to Shakespeare, the greatest writer in the English language, expose a crucial deficiency in the Brave New World. If science is to help humanity rather than to dominate and even dehumanise it, the novel implies, then science must accommodate art. Life without art, in no matter how advanced a technological context, is meaningless. The sacrifice of Shakespeare, whose work is 'prohibited' in the Brave New World (pp.51, 176), is, Mond admits, 'the price we have to pay for stability. You've got to choose between happiness and what people used to call high art. We've sacrificed the high art' (p.177).

There are, however, some questionable points regarding the use of the Shakespeare theme. For example, it is highly improbable that Pueblo Indians would have a volume of Shakespeare's complete works tucked conveniently away 'in one of the chests of the Antelope Kiva', yet that is where Linda found the copy she gave the Savage (p.110). It is also unclear how the Head Mistress of Eton has come to hear of Shakespeare (p.133), as 'all books published before AF 150', including those by 'a man called Shakespeare', have been suppressed (p.51) and 'Almost nobody', only 'the very few', such as Mustapha Mond, are allowed to read Shakespeare (p.176). But it is not always certain whether the reader is meant to take the Shakespeare allusions at face value or ironically. In other words, Shakespeare's art is put forward as a vitally necessary alternative to the Brave New World by means of the Savage's quotations, yet often these quotes reveal a misunderstanding of Shakespeare by the Savage. For instance, before Lenina attempts to seduce him, the Savage imagines her to be Juliet—and yet Lenina can hardly be said to possess the 'vestal modesty' the Savage attributes to her by way of quoting Romeo's words about Juliet (p.120). And when Lenina tries to seduce the Savage, he calls her an 'impudent strumpet!' (p.157), quoting Othello's epithet for Desdemona—yet Othello is, of course, tragically wrong about his faithfully innocent wife. Thus, when Shakespeare is termed the Savage's 'voice of conscience' (p.155), it is not clear whether the phrase is to be taken as a tribute to Shakespeare's art or as a revelation of the Savage's overly-moralistic mentality.

The characters

Bernard and the Savage

Two characters in *Brave New World*, Bernard Marx and the Savage, can be considered major characters in that the novel primarily follows their stories. Although different in significant ways, especially in that Bernard is a product of the Brave New World and the Savage a visitor to it, both are rebels and outcasts.

Unlike other members of the highest Brave New World caste, Alpha-Plus, Bernard, a specialist in sleep-teaching, is short, scrawny, and even 'ugly' (p.47), presumably because alcohol was poured into his blood-surrogate while he was still in the bottle (pp.47, 57, 60, 77, 82, 100, 128, 141). Hence, he is 'melancholy' (p.55) because his physical deficiencies 'isolated Bernard from his fellow men' (p.62). Moreover, Bernard's physical flaws have produced in him a 'mental excess' (pp.62, 63). Bernard is therefore unable to adjust to the rigid pattern of life thrust upon all Brave New Worlders, wanting instead something richer and more satisfying. For this reason he is unmoved by the Solidarity Service; seeks a deeper, more emotional relationship with Lenina than the World State allows; and is attracted to the two other characters with similar temperaments to his, Helmholtz and the Savage. The insecurity generated by his physical limitations, however, makes Bernard an unpleasant character in several respects. It causes him to alternate between arrogant 'boasting', for example, and 'abject self-pity' (p.86). It also causes Bernard to parade the Savage proudly before the Brave New World and to be jealous of the Savage's friendship with Helmholtz. Finally, Bernard's insecurity is responsible for his standing by passively 'in an agony of humiliated indecision' during the Savage's *soma* rebellion (p.172), and causes his betrayal of his friends before the World Controller (pp.181–2); in the end, however, by some unexplained means, Bernard's face reveals 'a new expression of determined resignation' (p.193).

In contrast to Bernard, the Savage is a splendid physical specimen, handsome and well-proportioned (p.99). But like Bernard, the Savage is an outcast, for his white skin, blond hair, and blue eyes (p.98) isolate him from the Red Indians among whom he was born. Indeed, his sense of being 'different' and for that reason of being 'lonely' leads him to identify with Bernard (p.114). His love of Shakespeare also gives him a kind of 'mental excess' similar to Bernard's. Again like Bernard, the Savage rejects the Brave New World's safe but drab efficiency for a riskier life of the spirit (p.192). But unlike the more timid Bernard, who represses his violent instincts (see, for example, p.53), the Savage is able to give vent to his rebellious energies against the Brave New World, as his *soma* revolt at Park Lane Hospital demonstrates. Yet the Savage, too, is not a wholly likeable character. For one thing, he is prudishly naive, projecting his idealised visions of virginity on to a woman, Lenina, whom they do not fit. The Savage also has an overwhelming Oedipal problem that paralyses him sexually. But certainly worst of all is his sado-masochism. He becomes violent with Lenina when she makes sexual advances to him, even threatening to kill her (p.157), and again becomes violent when she approaches him (at the end of the novel), slashing her with his whip 'like a madman' and shouting, 'kill it, kill it!' (p.205). He masochistically forces himself to vomit and flagellates himself with alarming regularity, and even, in the end, hangs himself.

Minor characters

Minor characters worth mentioning include Lenina Crowne, Mustapha Mond, and Helmholtz Watson. Lenina helps bridge the stories of Bernard and the Savage in that she is the object of both characters' affections. Although at the start of the novel she shows Henry Foster monogamous feelings of the sort forbidden in the Brave New World, she feels attracted in an almost maternal way to Bernard's inadequacies, and falls in love with the Savage immediately upon seeing him. Lenina appears frequently in the novel; but her generally conformist attitude towards Brave New World ways (for example, her enthusiasm for such trivial entertainments as obstacle golf and the feelies, her unfavourable reactions to the fertility rite at the Reservation and to Linda, and her habitual parroting of sleep-teaching slogans) prevents her from being interesting enough to be considered a major character.

As Resident Controller for Western Europe and therefore one of the ten World Controllers (p.38), Mustapha Mond serves chiefly to express the central beliefs of the Brave New World. This he does on two occasions, at the beginning of the narrative and, in greater detail, toward the end. Huxley attempts to flesh out Mond's character somewhat by revealing Mond's early heretical love of scientific truth (as opposed to the mindless Brave New World obsession with technology). Instead of rebelling, however, Mond chose to reject his forbidden quest for truth to become a World Controller (pp.181–3). It is not explained why whoever is in ultimate control of the World State put such faith in an admitted heretic as to place him in a position of great power. Nor, for that matter, is Mond's physical mediocrity explained—as an Alpha-Plus, Mond should be physically superior (pp.61–2), whereas in fact he is of only 'middle height' and does not seem to be particularly handsome (p.37). Thus, Mond serves as a counter to the three rebels, Bernard, the Savage, and Helmholtz: Mond's is the rebel spirit that has chosen to conform.

The most interesting of the minor characters is Helmholtz Watson, who could be considered a major character except for his relatively brief appearance in the novel. Physically and mentally a superb figure, Helmholtz is 'every centimetre an Alpha-Plus' (p.62). He excels in athletics and is an 'indefatigable lover' (p.62). Still, he yearns for a more spiritually rewarding life than the Brave New World offers, one that will allow full play to his latent poetic powers. Like those of his friends Bernard and the Savage, Helmholtz's attempts to realise his full human potential force him into conflict with the ruling powers of the Brave New World. But unlike his two friends, Helmholtz has no significant flaws in his character. Beyond dismissing some of Shakespeare on the basis of Brave New World standards (p.149), Helmholtz is flawless. 'Without a reproach, without a comment', Helmholtz forgives Bernard for boasting (p.145), and he keeps Bernard from breaking down completely even though Bernard has betrayed Helmholtz and the Savage (p.194). Helmholtz also assists the Savage in the *soma* rebellion (pp.171–2).

Flaws in characterisation

The most damaging criticism usually lodged against Huxley's characterisation in *Brave New World* (and, indeed, in his other novels) is that it is unconvincing. That is, most readers simply do not find the novel's characters very life-like and therefore have difficulty sympathising with or even being interested in them. This is not particularly surprising in that *Brave New World* is a novel that emphasises ideas rather than characters. Huxley himself admitted to having trouble in creating believable characters. Moreover, Huxley chose a theme that in fact virtually requires non-life-like characters. *Brave New World* tries to show that a technologically-dominated society that leaves no place for the arts dehumanises man by draining him of the spiritual essence that lifts him above beasthood. Hence, the Brave New Worlders are more like automatons than flesh-and-blood people, so that no matter how plausible or profound the novel's theme may be, from the perspective of characterisation, that theme produces aesthetic problems.

A novel without a hero?

It has become a critical commonplace to suggest that modern literature presents, not traditional heroes, but anti-heroes—badly flawed or even ignoble characters who lack the dignity, stature, and powers of conventional heroes. Certainly this is the case with *Brave New World*, one theme of the novel being that too much reliance on scientific technology robs man of his heroic possibilities. As Mustapha Mond says, 'civilisation has absolutely no need of nobility or heroism. These things are symptoms of political inefficiency. In a properly organised society, like ours, nobody has an opportunity for being noble or heroic' (p.190). Although Bernard is intellectually gifted and bravely rebellious, for instance, he is also frail, petty, egotistical, and deeply insecure. And the Savage, who is physically powerful, is foolishly naive, puritanical, and both sadistic and masochistic. Mond, another potential hero, has surrendered his magnificent intellectual gifts for political power. Thus, Huxley must necessarily reduce the least flawed character, Helmholtz Watson, to secondary status: too great a display of Helmholtz's vast powers would contradict one of the novel's main points.

Part 4

Hints for study

General suggestions

Your studying of *Brave New World*, as with most academic topics, will probably consist of two parts: *(i)* preparing to write an examination or a research paper; *(ii)* actually writing the examination (either in class or at home) or the paper. But no matter what the nature of the assignment, you will do well to keep several points in mind.

Above all else, there is no substitute for a thorough digestion of the novel. Read and re-read *Brave New World* as often as possible, actually thinking as you read about such central critical areas as theme, characterisation, plot, point of view, language, and setting. Learn to take notes as you read—mark off key passages that convey thematic material or help to shape characterisation; jot down recurring images, metaphors, and motifs; investigate the symbolic implications of speech, setting, and action; determine when narrative material is being presented ironically. You should also keep a good dictionary close at hand and refer to it whenever you are uncertain about the meaning of a word.

When you feel you have a fairly solid grasp of the novel, go back through it to try to see how the particulars you have thought about contribute to a total understanding of *Brave New World*. This last point is especially important: you should learn to consider the whole of the novel, that is, to avoid viewing the particulars in isolation and, instead, to see how they relate to the totality. You should not, for example, consider the episode presenting the Savage's *soma* rebellion simply as a piece of heightened action involving a fiery speech, a riot, and a comical arrest. Rather, you should ask yourself *why* Huxley has included the scene—what its function is in relation to other episodes, how he has integrated it into the narrative, how it helps to develop character and forward the action, and how it grows out of the preceding episode and leads into the episode that follows it.

If you read *Brave New World* carefully and think about it deliberately, you should be able to answer any examination question you are likely to be asked. In studying the novel, even if you are an advanced student, a good dictionary of literary terms is indispensable. After all, if you do not know what, for instance, 'point of view' is, you will be hard-pressed to write any kind of satisfactory answer to a question about the point of view of the novel.

Examinations

If *Brave New World* is on the syllabus of a literature course you are following, read the novel as carefully and as often as time permits during the week it is to be discussed. Then when you go back to study the novel for an examination, you already know a considerable amount about the book and can prepare for the examination rapidly and efficiently. On the other hand, if you put off reading and studying *Brave New World* until just before the examination (especially if you must also study other works) you will most likely find yourself overwhelmed and confused by the mass of material confronting you, which has to be assimilated under pressure.

When you receive the examination paper, read all the questions carefully. Select the question that you feel will most easily allow you to show what you know about *Brave New World*. Then go over the question you have selected with great care, making certain that you understand precisely what it is you are being asked to do. As you are writing your answer out, be sure that you are answering everything the question asks, and also that everything you write down helps in some way to answer it. You must also take care to be as concrete as possible— that is, to define abstractions and to support generalisations with specific examples from the text. Finally, reread your answer, correcting misspellings, clarifying obscure wordings, crossing out irrelevancies, and adding textual evidence where it is lacking.

If you have to write an examination in class, it is vital that you learn to allot your time sensibly. If, for instance, you are answering a question for which you are allowed thirty minutes and that requires you to do three equally important things, do not spend ten minutes introducing your subject and fifteen minutes on your first point, so that you are left with only five minutes on the last two points. Instead, give roughly equal time to each part of the question, say, seven to ten minutes, leaving a few minutes over for rereading. A good way to prepare yourself for writing within the time available in an examination is to make up an examination question, then to set an alarm clock for a half or a whole hour, and answer the question by the time the alarm sounds. Repeat this exercise until you are able to answer the question satisfactorily—and to reread your answer—within the time-limit.

Writing an essay

If you are going to write an essay on *Brave New World*, first make sure that you select a topic you can handle. If, for instance, you are interested in utopianism, do not choose as your topic '*Brave New World* and the utopian tradition', which would oblige you to read through and then relate to *Brave New World* the whole body of utopian literature. A more plausible choice would be a topic such as 'Huxley's *Brave New World* and George Orwell's *Nineteen Eighty-Four*: propaganda and force in two twentieth-century British dystopias'. Once you have selected a workable topic, you would do well to write out your own interpretation of the material you are dealing with before you consult any critics. This will help to ensure that your essay will be based on your own independent thinking, and not merely on what others have said about the novel. Then, when you do begin to read critics, evaluate their comments carefully. For example, does critic A actually buttress his arguments with textual evidence, or does he generalise without the use of supporting examples? Does he come to terms with textual material that contradicts his central idea, or does he simply ignore it in the hope that his reader will not notice? If you disagree with a particular critic, you will often find that the disagreement provides a convenient starting-point for your own argument. But in any event, learn to use critical material judiciously: show your reader that, having done your homework, so to speak, you are familiar with the major points of critical debate over *Brave New World*. On the other hand, avoid throwing into your essay any and every critical reference you can get your hands on because you think that a lengthy list of footnotes and a weighty bibliography will impress your reader—more likely, they will only irritate him and cause him to question your judgement. Even if you have had a course in essay writing, and especially if you have not, you will find a sound guide to the writing of essays useful. Such a guide will explain time-saving tips for using the library; key reference works; techniques for making note and bibliography cards; forms of citation; and proper manuscript preparation. Adhering to the established conventions of essay-writing will instil confidence in your reader that you know what you are doing; on the other hand, if the mechanics by means of which you present your material are shoddy or incorrect, the examiner is probably going to suspect that the essay's content is also questionable. Finally, even if you are not required to do so, type your paper if possible. Your examiner will have a number of other papers to mark, and he will appreciate a clean, easily-read copy. If he must stop periodically to puzzle out your handwriting, it is possible that he will lose the thread of your argument, and virtually certain that he will become irritated.

Study topics

Careful consideration of the topics listed below (as well as of those raised in Part 3) should prepare you to answer any question about *Brave New World* you are likely to be asked in an examination, and also generate ideas for a research paper on the novel.

Begin with the theme of *Brave New World*, the central point the narrative makes. Try to state in a single sentence what this theme is. Is the theme convincingly developed by a dynamic interaction of plot and character? Or is it stated baldly and undramatically in a didactic manner?

Who is the protagonist (the main character) of *Brave New World*? Who is the antagonist (the person or force against whom or which the protagonist must contend)? Is this conflict resolved, and if so, how? If not, why not?

The structure of *Brave New World* is unusual. The first three chapters are spent in lengthy exposition setting the scene for the forward action. What inherent feature in the setting of the novel has required the author to spend so much time on this preparation?

Is the tone of the story appropriate to the whole? Satire of the sort Huxley writes is often humorous—but is the novel sometimes *too* humorous in the light of the seriousness of the subject? Consider, for example, the comic satire on journalism that occupies several pages immediately before the Savage tragically hangs himself at the end of the novel. Notice that the episode at the Reservation is not humorous in tone—why?

How successful is the novel's language? Certainly it is often witty; but, as with the humorous tone, does the wit contribute to the total effect of *Brave New World*, or are there places where the author is unable to miss an opportunity to show how witty he can be, regardless of whether it is appropriate to the situation? Are the characters sufficiently distinguished by their language—their speech-patterns, vocabulary, and level of diction, for example? Or do the characters all sound alike? If certain words were read aloud to you, would you be able to determine which character's they were? Does the novel at times rely too heavily on language to carry meaning—that is, does it state its themes too obviously, rather than creating meaning through characterisation and action?

Are the major characters of *Brave New World* 'flat' or 'round'? That is, do some of them have only a single dimension, so that they are obviously 'good' or 'bad' people? Or are the characters genuinely alive and interesting people whose several character traits and whose internal struggles with complex moral issues make you concerned about what happens to them?

Consider the point of view (the angle of narration) of *Brave New World*. Is the point of view omniscient (that is, is the story told by an all-knowing, godlike narrator)? Or is it in whole or in part limited to the thoughts, feelings, and perceptions of a single character or of a few characters? Would the point of view of the novel be more effective if it were in some way different? Or is the point of view Huxley uses adequate for the materials it conveys?

If you are writing an essay on *Brave New World*, what are the chief points of agreement on the part of critics, and what critical considerations of the novel are the most controversial? Do some critics lose sight of literary criticism altogether and begin discussing the novel as social prophecy, or as if it were a political, philosophical, or religious essay, rather than a novel? What significant aspects of the novel have critics *not* discussed (thinking about these aspects may help you in finding an essay topic, or in limiting a general topic you already have)? What, in other words, can your work contribute to critical discussion of *Brave New World*?

Questions about *Brave New World*

Questions requiring shorter answers *(about 750 words or less)*

(1) Discuss the function of one of the following minor characters: Fanny Crowne; Henry Foster; Popé.

(2) Except for the Savage, who by birth stands outside the World State's class system, everyone in the Brave New World belongs to a pre-determined social-intellectual class. Analyse the caste system in *Brave New World*, determining what it contributes to the meaning of the novel.

(3) Imagine that *Brave New World* has been re-written so that its point of view is limited solely to the perspective of Helmholtz, or Bernard, or the Savage (select only one). In what significant ways do you think the novel would be different from the one Huxley wrote?

(4) It is only infrequently noticed by critics that, for all of *Brave New World*'s political overtones, Huxley avoids going into detail about the political machinery of the World State. Describe what political structure the novel does reveal, then try to explain why Huxley underplays the political element.

(5) *(i)* Explain what experimental technique is used in Chapter 3 of *Brave New World*; *(ii)* evaluate the success or failure of Huxley's use of this technique.

(6) Analyse the passage on pp.143–4 in which Mustapha Mond censors a paper entitled 'A New Theory of Biology', showing how the passage relates to the whole of the novel, and why Huxley has placed it where he has, instead of somewhere else in the novel.

(7) '*Brave New World* is a novel of the future full of local colour.' Discuss.

(8) The motif of time recurs regularly in the novel. Individual characters have a heightened awareness of time, clocks chime frequently, and all Brave New Worlders are afraid of old age. Investigate this theme.

(9) Huxley writes in the Foreword: 'The theme of *Brave New World* is not the advancement of science as such; it is the advancement of science as it affects human individuals.' Argue whether or not this quotation accurately reflects the totality of the novel.

(10) *(i)* Paraphrase the epigraph (that is, put it into your own words); *(ii)* relate the epigraph to the whole of *Brave New World.*

(11) Although genuine art has, of course, been banished from the World State, art is nonetheless a key subject in *Brave New World.* Develop a theory of art based upon the novel's ideas about this subject.

(12) Analyse Helmholtz Watson's poem on pp.146–7, then discuss its relevance to the novel.

(13) Music as subject matter is usually prominent in *Brave New World.* There are scraps of futuristic songs and lullabies; strange new synthetic instruments; formal musical terminology; even a reference to Mozart. Investigate the function of music in the novel.

(14) '*Brave New World* dramatises the age-old tension between the individual and society.' Discuss this view.

(15) Show how, in Chapter 11, the paragraph describing the Electrical Equipment Corporation—from 'And, in effect, eighty-three almost noseless black brachycephalic Deltas' to 'freckled Epsilon Semi-Morons'—effectively communicates the point Huxley wants to make.

Topics for essays

(1) Three of the major utopian works of the twentieth century are *Brave New World*, the Russian Yevgeny Zamyatin's *We* (1924), and George Orwell's *Nineteen Eighty-Four* (1949). Compare and contrast these three works.

(2) Study the Shakespearean allusions in *Brave New World*, analysing the appropriateness of each and evaluating the effectiveness of the allusions as a whole.

(3) Discuss *Brave New World* in the light of a consideration of *Brave New World Revisited* (1958).

(4) Investigate the literary debt Huxley owes in the writing of *Brave New World* to the novelist H. G. Wells.

(5) Compare and contrast *Brave New World* with Huxley's other utopian novels, *Ape and Essence* (1948) and *Island* (1962).

Hints for answering questions

Take Question (1) of the questions requiring shorter answers: 'Discuss the function of one of the following minor characters: Fanny Crowne; Henry Foster; Pope.' The first thing to do is to read the question carefully and determine precisely what you are being asked to do. Here, you must do one thing only: discuss the function of one (and not of two or all three) of the minor characters listed. Obviously, you will want to select for discussion that character about whom you have the most to say. Then you will want to *plan your answer*. Do not immediately begin writing down, as rapidly as you can, everything you can remember about the character you choose. Instead, try to organise your answer by determining a central idea or purpose that will serve as the focus for what you will write. Then think about material that will help to support your central idea, discarding anything that is not relevant to it. Sift out more important from less important material, and make sure that your answer will stress the more significant points. Only after you have a good idea of what you want to say and how you want to say it should you begin writing. If you have not at least jotted down a number of points or even constructed some form of outline, you almost certainly should not begin writing.

Assume, for instance, that, of the three characters the question allows you to choose among, Henry Foster is the one you remember the most about. You might begin by making notes of the following sort: 'H.F.—appears mostly in first part of novel; scientist—tells students about test-tube breeding; affair with Lenina (sex); date with L. (helicopter ride, dance at cabaret)'. Once you have quickly jotted this information down, you could then think about the purposes each item you have listed serves and arrive at a statement of the central idea of your answer: 'H.F.'s functions: (1) introduce scientific technology; (2) sexual theme; (3) show leisure-time activities (date with L.).' Finally, you will need to recall enough examples from the novel to support these general points adequately. (The degree to which you can be concrete will, of course, be higher if you are allowed to use your text in the examination. Even if you cannot use your text, provided you have studied the novel carefully enough, you should be able to remember sufficient information to answer the question convincingly.) After you have jotted down and organised key information, stated a central idea, and recalled enough supporting examples, you might produce an answer to this question similar to the following.

Specimen answer to Question 1

Henry Foster, a minor character in *Brave New World*, is not particularly interesting or even likeable. Nonetheless, an analysis of his main appearances in the novel will show that he makes three contributions: he helps to describe the scientific technology of AF 632; to establish the novel's sexual theme; and to provide 'local colour' about Brave New World entertainment.

Henry, who appears mainly in the first third of the novel, is introduced in the opening chapter, when the D.H.C. calls upon him to provide information for the students who are touring the Hatchery and Conditioning Centre. With great enthusiasm, Henry explains various technical procedures of the Fertilising, Bottling, Social Predestination, and Decanting Rooms. As the whole first chapter is devoted to establishing the scientific underpinnings of a society six hundred years in advance of the present day, the author must present the necessary facts and pseudo-facts both economically and dramatically. This Huxley does by means of the students' tour, guided first by the D.H.C. and then, for purposes of narrative variety, by Henry. Henry's first function, then, is to help set the scene for the main action of the story.

Henry next appears as part of the montage of the experimentally-written third chapter. A central purpose of this chapter, which opens with a group of naked children playing erotic games, is to reveal the warped promiscuity of the Brave New World's sexual values. Henry's dialogue in the Men's Dressing-Room with the Assistant Predestinator helps to expose these values. Henry's intense interest in his colleague's description of a sensually realistic love-scene from the feelies, and his enthusiastic efforts to convince the Assistant Predestinator to 'have' the 'pneumatic' Lenina, disclose the cheap regard the World State's citizens have for sex. Henry's parroting of the sleep-teaching slogan 'Everyone belongs to everyone else' accurately summarises his society's sexual values.

Finally, Henry's date with Lenina, which occurs later on the same day as the events in the above two paragraphs, is described in Part 1 of Chapter 4 and Part 1 of Chapter 5. We have already had a view of Brave New World life during working hours, and the narrative purpose of this date is to show in a concise manner what Brave New World life is like after hours. In Chapter 4, as Henry pilots Lenina in his helicopter to Stoke Poges for a few rounds of obstacle golf, we are given a panorama of suburban London as it has been altered by six hundred years of presumed 'progress'. We are shown several types of Brave New World games and watch the various lower-caste members scurrying to or from work by various means of transportation. The first part of the next chapter presents in some detail an evening's entertainment in futuristic London. But first, Henry and Lenina's flight back from Stoke Poges provides the perspective for another brief panorama of different aspects of Brave New World life, with special attention given to the highly efficient crematorium. After dinner and *soma*, Henry escorts Lenina to the cabaret that Westminster Abbey has been converted into, where they dance with hundreds of other drugged couples to loud and sensuous synthetic music. Inevitably, the evening concludes with Henry inviting Lenina into his bed. Henry's date with Lenina, then, affords a focal point for a portrayal of several facets, especially entertainment, of the Brave New World that assist in familiarising us with life in AF 632. Moreover, Henry's racing with Lenina from a trivial game of golf to a self-indulgent form of musical entertainment reveals the mindless waste of leisure-time in the Brave New World.

These three episodes are linked by satire. Henry's pride in and enthusiasm for the inhuman technology of his work; his impersonal approach to sex; and his zealous participation in meaningless leisure-time activities are all mocked by Huxley. Henry appears, but only briefly, twice more in the story: at the start of Chapter 13, when he helps to show Lenina's distress over her rejection by the Savage; and at the end, when he flees the violent Savage, leaving Lenina at his mercy. But the three earlier episodes are the crucial ones for understanding Henry's function in *Brave New World*.

Comment on the specimen answer

This answer states its purpose clearly and develops its argument logically and consistently. Although direct quotations from the novel have been avoided, the answer nonetheless provides specific details that help explain and illustrate its points. By reference to satire, the concluding paragraph connects the three main points that support the essay's central idea. But, because this last paragraph concludes by referring back to the central idea, special emphasis is given to the writer's main point.

Specimen answer to Question 10: *(i)* Paraphrase the epigraph (that is, put it into your own words); *(ii)* relate the epigraph to the whole of *Brave New World*.

The epigraph from Berdiaeff may be paraphrased as follows: It would appear that utopias are much more 'realisable' than people previously thought. Today, we have to face the 'alarming question' of how to avoid the complete realisation of utopias. 'Utopias are realisable', and life moves towards them. Maybe we are at the dawn of a new century when people will figure out ways to avoid utopias, and to return to a society more free because it is less 'perfect'.

Huxley would agree with Berdiaeff that utopias are realisable. Huxley has himself 'realised' a future utopia in *Brave New World*; and in another novel, *Island*, he describes a utopia set in the present day. These two novels, however, are radically different. *Brave New World* presents a negative utopia, a 'dystopia', whereas *Island* portrays a truly perfect, utopian society. What is frightening is that neither novel provides a functional basis for a life that is both free and secure. In *Brave New*

World the people have all the security they want, and, indeed, even more of it than some of them desire; but they lack the freedom of self-expression, as Helmholtz's trouble with the authorities over his poem on solitude demonstrates. In *Island*, on the other hand, the people are spiritually free; but they are not secure from the destructive forces of the materialistic outside world, which in the end moves in to crush them.

But, as Berdiaeff points out, an important question is how to avoid a complete utopia, one in which life is so perfect that significant achievement by individuals is unnecessary. Such a 'complete utopia' is what Huxley delineates in *Brave New World*. In futuristic London, nobody grows old or becomes fat; there is no crime, poverty, or unemployment; the senses are freely indulged in; and, in the unlikely event that any problem should arise, a dose of *soma* will soothe it away. But Huxley's point is that, precisely because there are no problems, there is nothing worthwhile for anybody to do. For this reason, Bernard and Helmholtz, and probably other Brave New Worlders as well, find themselves unhappy, paradoxically, because there is nothing for them to be unhappy about. This, then, is a central irony of the novel: utopia is actually dystopian for the very reason that it is utopian. In other words, man has always struggled to solve his problems; but were he ever to do this in reality, as the World State in *Brave New World* has done, he would create for himself the greatest problem of all: meaninglessness.

Comment on specimen answer to Question 10

This answer is not satisfactory because most of it fails to answer the question as it is asked. The question requires two things: first, a paraphrase of the epigraph; and second, a discussion of the relationship between the epigraph and *Brave New World*. But the writer of this answer does not actually paraphrase the epigraph by recasting Berdiaeff's words into his own. Instead, the writer merely shuffles some of Berdiaeff's words around, or even quotes Berdiaeff directly, and generally follows Berdiaeff's own sentence structures. On the whole, the first paragraph of the answer is closer to plagiarism than it is to paraphrase.

Furthermore, the second paragraph of the answer does not relate the epigraph to the whole of *Brave New World*. Although it does use the epigraph as a starting-point, it launches into a comparison and contrast of *Brave New World* and another of Huxley's novels, *Island*. The third paragraph is the most successful. It not only uses one of the ideas Berdiaeff presents in the epigraph as a point of departure, it also develops the idea by applying it only to *Brave New World*.

Specimen answer to Question 15: Show how, in Chapter 11, the paragraph describing the Electrical Equipment Corporation—from 'And, in effect, eighty-three almost noseless black brachycephalic Deltas' to 'freckled Epsilon Semi-Morons'—effectively communicates the point Huxley wants to make.

During his tour of the Electrical Equipment Corporation, the Savage witnesses lower-caste factory workers carrying out their various duties. 'Each process,' he is told, 'is carried out, so far as possible, by a single Bokanovsky Group,' each of which consists of numerous identical twins. The negative effect this sight has on the Savage is emphasised by the language used in this paragraph, which describes the groups of twins at work. Two linguistic devices that help the reader to understand why the Savage becomes nauseated by what he sees are: firstly, repetition, both of numbers and of syntax; and, secondly, drab, unadorned imagery that is purely functional in nature.

The frequent repetition of numbers in the paragraph is striking. In a paragraph of slightly more than 150 words, twenty numbers are used. About one word in eight, then, is a number, an unusually high percentage. One particularly unusual feature of the paragraph is that numbers are repeated even when the quantity of the items to which the numbers refer is already clear. Thus, numbers are sometimes repeated solely for the sake of repetition: 'The fifty-six four-spindle chucking and turning machines were being manipulated by fifty-six aquiline and ginger Gammas'; 'forty-seven blond heads were confronted by forty-seven brown ones. Forty-seven snubs by forty-seven hooks; forty-seven receding by forty-seven prognathous chins.' Moreover, almost everything mentioned is specifically numbered. There are not simply 'low work-tables,' for example, or even 'a few low work-tables', but 'two low work-tables'. The effect of this repetition of numbers is to suggest a society in which numbers have come to matter as much as, or even more than, people. No single individuals are mentioned, only groups of numbered but anonymous workers. Thus the humanity of the workers has been overwhelmed by the numbers to which it has been sacrificed. Indeed, numbers have become more important than people to the extent that Brave New Worlders are even bred to size: the thirty-three Delta screw-cutters, for example, are 'all within 20 millimetres of 1 metre 69 centimetres tall', presumably because that height is ideal for the work they were test-tube bred to do. The repetition of numbers also implies that the distinction between machines and human beings has become unimportant or even non-existent in the Brave New World: 'The fifty-six four-spindle chucking and turning machines were being manipulated by fifty-six aquiline and ginger Gammas.'

And not only are numbers repeated, but—as the above example

demonstrates—syntactic structures are also repeated, to help dissolve any distinction between machine and worker. In this instance, the construction of the first noun phrase, which refers to machinery, of numerical adjective (fifty-six), compound adjective (four-spindle chucking and turning), plural noun (machines) is repeated by the second, which refers to people, of numerical adjective (fifty-six), compound adjective (aquiline and ginger), plural noun (Gammas). This type of syntactical parallelism is used several times in the paragraph, for example in the presentation of the two groups of forty-seven Gamma-Plus dwarfs. The effect Huxley creates for the reader is one of monotonous reduplication, which is precisely the effect of deadening sameness that nauseates the Savage.

A sparse, undecorative type of purely functional imagery is another device of language in the paragraph that suggests the stifling, life-killing uniformity of Brave New World existence. The paragraph's imagery is used to represent both the factory's machinery and its workers. Firstly, the factory machinery is described in language that can be termed technical or businesslike. The adjectives applied to the machines are meant to describe them in an efficiently objective, functional, ungarnished manner. Thus, the factory contains 'fifty-six four-spindle chucking and turning machines', 'two low work-tables' that 'faced one another', 'dynamos', and a 'conveyor with its load of separate parts', all geared to the production of 'completed mechanisms'. Although the imagery used to portray the factory workers is more ornamental, in that it is more colourful than that used to describe the factory's machinery, the added ornamentality serves, ironically, only to distinguish from each other the numerous groups of otherwise indistinguishable identical twins. There are, for example, 'black Deltas', 'aquiline and ginger Gammas', 'curly auburn girls in Gamma green', 'blue-eyed, flaxen and freckled Epsilon Semi-Morons'. Otherwise, the workers, like the machines they man, are described in functionally technical, businesslike terms: 'brachycephalic Deltas'; 'heat-conditioned Epsilon Senegalese'; 'Delta females' who are 'long-headed, sandy, with narrow pelvises, and all within 20 millimetres of 1 metre 69 centimetres tall'; 'Gamma-Plus dwarfs' with 'prognathous chins'. The point implied is, once again, that the Brave New World makes little or no distinction between machines and human beings, for both can be described by means of functional, clinical imagery.

On the whole, then, this paragraph presents a linguistic analogue to the thematic point that the technological advances of the Brave New World have been made at the expense of individual human beings. Because in surveying the factory scene the Savage perceives that vital differences between man and machine have been substantially wiped out, so that the workers resemble, and perhaps in a sense even become, the machines they run, he repeats with bitter irony Miranda's innocent statement in *The Tempest*, 'O brave new world that has such people in it.' Moreover, the numerical and syntactical repetitions and the use of unembellished imagery duplicate linguistically another of *Brave New World*'s fundamental ideas that the Savage learns: a mechanical mode of life, void of aesthetic beauty, is monotonous, drab, and even dehumanising.

Write your own commentary on the above answer to Question 15, concentrating on whether the essay actually does answer the question; supports its generalisations with textual evidence; avoids irrelevancies; is well-organised (that is, unified and coherent).

Part 5

Suggestions for further reading

The text

HUXLEY, ALDOUS: *Brave New World*, Panther Books, Granada, London, 1977. A paperback edition of *Brave New World* that is both inexpensive and easily obtainable. A comparable edition has been published in America by Harper & Row, New York, 1965. A more expensive American paperback edition is *Brave New World* and *Brave New World Revisited*, Harper & Row, New York, 1969.

The standard hardbound text of *Brave New World* is published in the Collected Edition by Chatto & Windus, London, and Harper & Row, New York.

Other relevant works by Aldous Huxley

Among Aldous Huxley's vast output of non-fiction, two titles will be particularly useful to the student of *Brave New World*: they are *Brave New World Revisited*, Chatto & Windus, London, 1972 (Collected Edition); an American paperback edition is published by Harper & Row, New York, 1965; and *Collected Essays*, Harper & Bros., New York, 1959 (not published in England; no Collected Edition).

Books about Aldous Huxley

The last fifteen years have witnessed an outburst of critical activity on Huxley, accompanied by a rise in his artistic reputation. Generally, recent critics have attempted to analyse and appreciate Huxley's literary techniques, rather than (as earlier critics tended to do) to emphasise his ideas. The following books give some indication of the type of critical material available on Huxley; most of these works contain bibliographies.

SMITH, GROVER (ED.): *Letters of Aldous Huxley*, Chatto & Windus, London, 1969. Some letters on *Brave New World*.

CLARK, RONALD W.: *The Huxleys*, Heinemann, London, 1968. Biographical; discusses Aldous Huxley in the context of the remarkable Huxley family.

WATT, DONALD (ED.): *Aldous Huxley: The Critical Heritage*, Routledge & Kegan Paul, London, 1975. Contains several reviews of *Brave New World* and an Introduction on the reception and reputation of Huxley's works.

PLIMPTON, GEORGE (ED.): *Writers at Work: The* Paris Review *Interviews*, second series, Viking, New York, 1963. This contains an interview with Huxley.

KUEHN, ROBERT E. (ED.): *Aldous Huxley: A Collection of Critical Essays*, Prentice-Hall, Englewood Cliffs, New Jersey, 1974. Although, curiously, there is no sustained discussion of *Brave New World* in this collection, some of its material on Huxley's thought and literary methods is helpful, especially Frederick J. Hoffman's essay, 'Aldous Huxley and the Novel of Ideas'.

Two examples of different critical approaches to Huxley are:

BIRNBAUM, MILTON: *Aldous Huxley's Quest for Values*, University of Tennessee Press, Knoxville, 1971. This draws frequently on Huxley's non-fiction to discuss numerous aspects of his ideas and beliefs.

MAY, KEITH M.: *Aldous Huxley*, Elek, London, 1972. This study is concerned with fictional techniques rather than with ideas; it is well-written and especially good on the structure and language of *Brave New World*.

The author of these notes

MICHAEL ROUTH was educated at California State University, Long Beach, and at the University of Wisconsin, where he was awarded a Ph.D. in 1973. He is a Lecturer in English at the University of Utrecht and has written the York Notes on Graham Greene's *Brighton Rock*.

York Notes: list of titles

CHINUA ACHEBE
Things Fall Apart
EDWARD ALBEE
Who's Afraid of Virginia Woolf?
ANONYMOUS
Beowulf
Everyman
W. H. AUDEN
Selected Poems
JANE AUSTEN
Emma
Mansfield Park
Northanger Abbey
Persuasion
Pride and Prejudice
Sense and Sensibility
SAMUEL BECKETT
Waiting for Godot
ARNOLD BENNETT
The Card
JOHN BETJEMAN
Selected Poems
WILLIAM BLAKE
Songs of Innocence, Songs of Experience
ROBERT BOLT
A Man For All Seasons
HAROLD BRIGHOUSE
Hobson's Choice
ANNE BRONTË
The Tenant of Wildfell Hall
CHARLOTTE BRONTË
Jane Eyre
EMILY BRONTË
Wuthering Heights
ROBERT BROWNING
Men and Women
JOHN BUCHAN
The Thirty-Nine Steps
JOHN BUNYAN
The Pilgrim's Progress
BYRON
Selected Poems
GEOFFREY CHAUCER
Prologue to the Canterbury Tales
The Clerk's Tale
The Franklin's Tale
The Knight's Tale
The Merchant's Tale
The Miller's Tale
The Nun's Priest's Tale

The Pardoner's Tale
The Wife of Bath's Tale
Troilus and Criseyde
SAMUEL TAYLOR COLERIDGE
Selected Poems
SIR ARTHUR CONAN DOYLE
The Hound of the Baskervilles
WILLIAM CONGREVE
The Way of the World
JOSEPH CONRAD
Heart of Darkness
STEPHEN CRANE
The Red Badge of Courage
BRUCE DAWE
Selected Poems
DANIEL DEFOE
Moll Flanders
Robinson Crusoe
WALTER DE LA MARE
Selected Poems
SHELAGH DELANEY
A Taste of Honey
CHARLES DICKENS
A Tale of Two Cities
Bleak House
David Copperfield
Great Expectations
Hard Times
Oliver Twist
The Pickwick Papers
EMILY DICKINSON
Selected Poems
JOHN DONNE
Selected Poems
GERALD DURRELL
My Family and Other Animals
GEORGE ELIOT
Middlemarch
Silas Marner
The Mill on the Floss
T. S. ELIOT
Four Quartets
Murder in the Cathedral
Selected Poems
The Cocktail Party
The Waste Land
J. G. FARRELL
The Siege of Krishnapur
WILLIAM FAULKNER
The Sound and the Fury

HENRY FIELDING
  Joseph Andrews
  Tom Jones
F. SCOTT FITZGERALD
  Tender is the Night
  The Great Gatsby
GUSTAVE FLAUBERT
  Madame Bovary
E. M. FORSTER
  A Passage to India
  Howards End
JOHN FOWLES
  The French Lieutenant's Woman
JOHN GALSWORTHY
  Strife
MRS GASKELL
  North and South
WILLIAM GOLDING
  Lord of the Flies
  The Spire
OLIVER GOLDSMITH
  She Stoops to Conquer
  The Vicar of Wakefield
ROBERT GRAVES
  Goodbye to All That
GRAHAM GREENE
  Brighton Rock
  The Heart of the Matter
  The Power and the Glory
WILLIS HALL
  The Long and the Short and the Tall
THOMAS HARDY
  Far from the Madding Crowd
  Jude the Obscure
  Selected Poems
  Tess of the D'Urbervilles
  The Mayor of Casterbridge
  The Return of the Native
  The Woodlanders
L. P. HARTLEY
  The Go-Between
NATHANIEL HAWTHORNE
  The Scarlet Letter
SEAMUS HEANEY
  Selected Poems
ERNEST HEMINGWAY
  A Farewell to Arms
  The Old Man and the Sea
SUSAN HILL
  I'm the King of the Castle
BARRY HINES
  Kes
HOMER
  The Iliad
  The Odyssey

GERARD MANLEY HOPKINS
  Selected Poems
TED HUGHES
  Selected Poems
ALDOUS HUXLEY
  Brave New World
HENRIK IBSEN
  A Doll's House
HENRY JAMES
  The Portrait of a Lady
  Washington Square
BEN JONSON
  The Alchemist
  Volpone
JAMES JOYCE
  A Portrait of the Artist as a Young Man
  Dubliners
JOHN KEATS
  Selected Poems
PHILIP LARKIN
  Selected Poems
D. H. LAWRENCE
  Selected Short Stories
  Sons and Lovers
  The Rainbow
  Women in Love
HARPER LEE
  To Kill a Mocking-Bird
LAURIE LEE
  Cider with Rosie
CHRISTOPHER MARLOWE
  Doctor Faustus
HERMAN MELVILLE
  Moby Dick
THOMAS MIDDLETON and
  WILLIAM ROWLEY
  The Changeling
ARTHUR MILLER
  A View from the Bridge
  Death of a Salesman
  The Crucible
JOHN MILTON
  Paradise Lost I & II
  Paradise Lost IV & IX
  Selected Poems
V. S. NAIPAUL
  A House for Mr Biswas
ROBERT O'BRIEN
  Z for Zachariah
SEAN O'CASEY
  Juno and the Paycock
GEORGE ORWELL
  Animal Farm
  Nineteen Eighty-four

JOHN OSBORNE
Look Back in Anger
WILFRED OWEN
Selected Poems
ALAN PATON
Cry, The Beloved Country
THOMAS LOVE PEACOCK
Nightmare Abbey and *Crotchet Castle*
HAROLD PINTER
The Caretaker
SYLVIA PLATH
Selected Works
PLATO
The Republic
ALEXANDER POPE
Selected Poems
J. B. PRIESTLEY
An Inspector Calls
WILLIAM SHAKESPEARE
A Midsummer Night's Dream
Antony and Cleopatra
As You Like It
Coriolanus
Hamlet
Henry IV Part I
Henry IV Part II
Henry V
Julius Caesar
King Lear
Macbeth
Measure for Measure
Much Ado About Nothing
Othello
Richard II
Richard III
Romeo and Juliet
Sonnets
The Merchant of Venice
The Taming of the Shrew
The Tempest
The Winter's Tale
Troilus and Cressida
Twelfth Night
GEORGE BERNARD SHAW
Arms and the Man
Candida
Pygmalion
Saint Joan
The Devil's Disciple
MARY SHELLEY
Frankenstein
PERCY BYSSHE SHELLEY
Selected Poems
RICHARD BRINSLEY SHERIDAN
The Rivals

R. C. SHERRIFF
Journey's End
JOHN STEINBECK
Of Mice and Men
The Grapes of Wrath
The Pearl
LAURENCE STERNE
A Sentimental Journey
Tristram Shandy
TOM STOPPARD
Professional Foul
Rosencrantz and Guildenstern are Dead
JONATHAN SWIFT
Gulliver's Travels
JOHN MILLINGTON SYNGE
The Playboy of the Western World
TENNYSON
Selected Poems
W. M. THACKERAY
Vanity Fair
J. R. R. TOLKIEN
The Hobbit
MARK TWAIN
Huckleberry Finn
Tom Sawyer
VIRGIL
The Aeneid
ALICE WALKER
The Color Purple
KEITH WATERHOUSE
Billy Liar
EVELYN WAUGH
Decline and Fall
JOHN WEBSTER
The Duchess of Malfi
OSCAR WILDE
The Importance of Being Earnest
THORNTON WILDER
Our Town
TENNESSEE WILLIAMS
The Glass Menagerie
VIRGINIA WOOLF
Mrs Dalloway
To the Lighthouse
WILLIAM WORDSWORTH
Selected Poems
WILLIAM WYCHERLEY
The Country Wife
W. B. YEATS
Selected Poems